CW00551183

A POCKETFUL OF HOPS

HOP GROWING IN THE BROMYARD AREA

A new edition

THE BROMYARD AND DISTRICT LOCAL HISTORY SOCIETY
BROMYARD
HEREFORDSHIRE
2007

A Pocketful of Hops. Hop Growing in the Bromyard Area, A New Edition (2007)
© The Bromyard and District Local History Society
5 Sherford Street, Bromyard, HR7 4DL

www.bromyard.historysociety.org.uk

ISBN: 978-0-9546212-2-3

|||||||||||||||||||||||||||||||||||

9 780954 621223

ISBN-10: 0 9546212-2-0
ISBN-13: 978-0-9546212-2-3

Set in Times New Roman and printed in Great Britain by
Orphans Press, Leominster, Herefordshire HR6 8JT

Cover Illustrations:

*Front: A group of pickers in a polework hopyard near Ledbury early in the 20th century.
David Postle.*

*Back: A Pattenden Wren picking machine at work on dwarf hops at Dormington.
Peter Glendinning.*

Other publications of The Bromyard and District Local History Society:

* *Bromyard: A Local History* (1970)
* *Bromyard Parish Registers* by E D Pearson (1974)
* *Bromyard: The Day Before Yesterday* A book of photographs (1979)
* *Whitbourne: A Bishop's Manor* by P Williams (1979)
* *Little Cowarne: A Herefordshire Village* by J Hopkinson (1983)
* *Herefordshire Under Arms* by C Hopkinson (1985)
* *Bromyard: Minster, Manor And Town* by P Williams (1987)
* *A Pocketful of Hops. Hop Growing in the Bromyard Area* (1988)
Bromyard: Round and About by D Waller (1991)
Two Churches: Two Communities. St Peter's Bromyard and St James's Stanford Bishop
by E D Pearson (1993)
A History of Bredenbury and its Landed Estate by Jennifer Weale (1997)
Avenbury and the ruined church of St Mary by P Williams (2000)
Where Have All The Courts Gone? A monograph by J Hopkinson (2003)
The Churches of the Bromyard Rural Deanery An Informal Guide by D M Annett (2003)
Bromyard's Victorian Heritage A book of photographs (2005)
The Three Stanfords by P Williams (2007)

* OUT OF PRINT

CONTENTS

A POCKETFUL OF HOPS

Cover illustration of original edition, 1988.

MAPS

GRAPHS

TABLES

INTRODUCTION

A Pocketful of Hops has been one of the most successful books published by the Bromyard and District Local History Society. It has sold throughout the country and around the world. When stocks finally ran out in 2004 it was found that there was a continuing demand.

The Publications Committee of the Society therefore undertook to examine the possibility of a reprint or a revised edition. As it was nearly twenty years since the book was produced it was felt that a straightforward reprint was inappropriate. However, while it was necessary to bring the story up to date, it was important to retain the flavour of the original book.

To fulfil this purpose we have edited the original text, re-written it where necessary and augmented it with the story of hop-growing as it is at the start of the 21st century. Illustrations have also been reviewed and new maps and graphs have been introduced.

We have been lucky to be able to call upon two members of the original expert team: Peter Walker and Harry Paske, both hop farmers in the past. They were joined by Joan Grundy who has brought first-hand experience of the work of Rosemaund Experimental Husbandry Farm (EHF) and wide knowledge of the industry. Together these three have borne the brunt of textual correction and addition, the refinement of statistics and the selection of new photographs. The expertise of this team in modern computer skills has made the task significantly less onerous. The Society would like to record their thanks for the time, effort and knowledge which this team has devoted to this production.

We must also thank Joan Grundy for inviting Peter Glendinning to write the new chapter on dwarf hops and to provide appropriate photographs. It is a very authoritative overview of this recent development and we are most grateful for his contribution.

Once again we owe sincere thanks to the team at Orphans Press of Leominster. We have always been received with unlimited courtesy and patience.

In the introduction to the 1988 edition we wrote:

'Hops, hop growing. What on earth is the Bromyard and District Local History Society doing in bringing out a book on this subject which is more in keeping with agriculture? One must have lived in a hop-growing area to understand the importance that this crop once had, not only for the farmers but also for the community at large.'

The speed of change has, if anything, accelerated and the development of dwarf varieties of hop has encouraged determined and dedicated hop farmers to continue this activity. Many factors have influenced the reduction in the acreage of hops grown, the result being that it is now uncommon to see a hopyard in this part of Herefordshire. Where they have survived, the hop drying kilns have often been converted into desirable country dwellings, although in many cases the cowls have been retained, but are now fixed.

Modern harvesting no longer requires numerous hands nor the services that supported them. The hutment barracks for hop pickers which at one time were widespread can now hardly be seen. Charles Grant's sketches are evocative of times long past.

Some photographs in the original edition were published by permission of their owners and they are acknowledged in the original list. New photographs are attributed to their donors, otherwise, to the best of our knowledge, all the rest come from the archives of the Society. If there should be any which are used inadvertently without the owner's permission, I can only apologise.

In addition to those people mentioned above, Peter Mesdag has held a watching brief over costs and Mary Walker has kept notes at our meetings. On behalf of the Society I thank them all for their effort and commitment.

Hugh Langrishe; Chairman, Publications Committee, 2007

Spray of Wye Pioneer, a dwarf hop variety.   *Peter Glendinning*

ACKNOWLEDGEMENTS, 1988

The Bromyard and District Local History Society wishes to thank everyone who has helped with such enthusiasm and generosity to produce *A Pocketful of Hops*. This book would never have been embarked upon had it not been for the need to record some of the fund of knowledge displayed by the late Inett Homes in his talks to the Society; he and Harry Paske have been the major contributors on the history and the growing and drying of hops.

Additional material and local memories have come from Rene Andrews, Jack Blandford, Gilbert Bowler, Neston Capper, Kay Carey, Michael Carey, Eithne Crosskey, Philip Crosskey, Doll Courtney, Margaret Dallow, Daphne Davies, Irene Davies, Vera Davies, Gladys Draper, Layton Edwards, Dorothy Evans, Jack Fowler, Jean Hopkinson, Gilbert Hyde, Joan Leese, Suzanne Lowden, Neil Parker, Ethel Paske, Gwenllian Paske, Mary Essex Potter, Richard Essex Potter, John Pudge, Bill Rollason, Mildred Shepherd, Edith Silcock, Peter Walker, Deborah Waller, Mollie Walwyn, Phyllis Williams, Hester Wright, Lawson Wright, and many others. Eileen Holloway lent the diaries of her husband, the late Ted Holloway of Lower House, Stanford Bishop, and Norah Taber found the photographs to go with them; Marnie Caine and Brenda Swann copied the crop returns in the Public Record Office.

The following individuals and organisations have also provided information and help: B. J. Whitehouse and the staff at Hereford Library; Sue Hubbard and her staff at Hereford Record Office; The Museum of Cider, Hereford; Keith Worsely, Horticultural Adviser with the Agricultural Development and Advisory Service; The Brewers' Society; John Lander and Alan Meredith, English Hops Ltd.; Morris Hanbury Jackson Le May Ltd., International Hop Merchants, Factors and Processors; Richard Rayer, hop merchant of Worcester; The Bruff Company; Bill and Phil Wargent; Norman Ham, former marketing manager of Pikes, Sons & Co.; R. C. Alford and the staff of A. & E. Pettifer Ltd, Bromyard; and numerous other growers, factors and merchants.

Lack of space has prevented the printing of more than a few of the many letters and photographs that have been received from the Black Country and South Wales, but all the letters, together with photocopies of photographs, have been deposited in the Bromyard Library where they will make a valuable archive for future reference. [They are now in the archives of the Bromyard Local History Society.] The Society is grateful to the writers:

L. R. Baker, P. A. Banner, J. M. Baxter, Mrs Beresford, I. Bill, H. Brooker, M. Brown, B. Butler, V. Chilton, D. Cox, F. Craddock, W. Crook, M. Fownes, D. Goodwin, F. Gordon, I. Griffiths, J. Grinsell, E. H. Hall, R. I. C. Hassell, S. Haydon, M. L. Hicklin, D. Horton, B. Howard, J. Hunt, C. James, R. Jennings, B. Johnson, E. Keay, F. Kofack, R. Leith, J. Lingard, E. Lloyd, V. L., D. J. Oliver, J. Owen, C. Palmer, H. E. Palmer, D. Pardoe, W. H. Parish, C. Parkes,

H. Parsons. E. Payne, J. Penty, C. Perry, F. Porter, G. D. Price, G. N. Price, P. S. Ray, H. Richardson, J. Scholfield, W. K. Scott, O. Shelton, M. Skidmore, M. Smith, W. C. Smith, D. A. Spinks, T. E. Taylor, C. J. Tyler, B. Wheeler, K. Whetstone.

Most of the other photographs are from the Society's own collection, built up by Daphne Davies and Deborah Waller from, among other sources, unique family prints lent to the Society for copying. The Society is indebted to everyone else who has given us permission to use their photographs, in particular Arthur and Elsie Berry, James Bomford, Leslie Bowcott, Bert Brookes, Basil Butcher, Martin Hewitt, Henry Hodges, Adam Jones, Robert Jones, Anne Orgee, Harry Paske, Madeleine Pudge and Ethel Waldron; Barbara Rhys for the lower photograph on page 105 from the Miss Wight Collection in Hereford Record Office; Hereford City Museum for the photograph on page 4 and Berrow's Newspapers for the one on page 77; and apologises for any photographs used inadvertently without the owner's permission. John Kinsman, Stephen Saunders and Edwin John copied many of the prints for publication.

The plan on page 92 and the line drawings are the work of Charles Grant, while the map on page 19 was prepared by Peter Russell.

The Society wishes to thank Birmingham University Extra Mural Group led by J. W. Tonkin, F.S.A., for permission to reproduce the plan drawn by Inett Homes on page 88, and Kay Bright and B. T. Batsford Ltd for their permission to print Geoffrey Bright's poem *Hops*.

Michael and Kay Carey, Charles Hopkinson and Colin Macdiarmid have read the manuscript with the eyes of those who previously knew little of hop growing, and have made many pertinent comments and helpful suggestions on how to present such diverse material.

Finally, Tony Hicks of Orphans Press Ltd has, once again, shown his expertise and customary patience in printing this the latest of the Society's publications.

Publication Committee

Philip Crosskey (*chairman*), Jean Hopkinson (*editor*).

Daphne Davies, Lynda Duthy-James, Joan Leese, Suzanne Lowden, Ethel Paske, Harry Paske, Bill Rollason, Mildred Shepherd, Deborah Waller, Phyllis Williams.

ACKNOWLEDGEMENTS, 2007

The Society also thanks the following for their help with this new edition: John Andrews of Western Quality Hops Ltd.; Ray Marriott of Botanix Ltd.; John Pudge of English Hops and Herbs Ltd.; Ray Pudge; Tony Redsell; Alan Unwin of Wealden Hops.

HOPS

When morning mists in Autumn, weave patterns in the vale,
And heavy dews that hint at frost, the lush green meadows pale;
And sheaves of corn in barn and rick, declare the harvest home,
Men still have hops to gather, down by the River Froome.

From many a smoke drenched city, from many a dreary slum,
From many a gaunt Welsh mining town, the pale faced families come,
By train and bus to Ledbury Town, excited, noisy, gay,
The happiest time in their drab lives-a holiday with pay.

Along the roads of England, from Lancashire to Kent,
Across the lonely mountain tracks, of Cumbria and Gwent,
The gypsy vans with yellow sides, red wheels, tarpaulin tops,
Are hurrying down to Bishop's Froome, to pick the golden hops.

As soon as chill September morn is warmed by mounting sun,
Deserted vans and barns denote that picking has begun;
In yards where golden bosses shine, against the broad green leaves,
Cascading from the taut straight wire, to which each tendril cleaves.

The serried, shady, dark green aisles, so orderly since May,
Become untidy heaps of bine, increasing day by day,
Till pole and wire stand bare and gaunt, against the Autumn sky,
From Withington to Ledbury Town, from Hegdon Hill to Wye.

Throughout the month, while picking lasts, that tranquil countryside,
Becomes a hive of industry, from morn to eventide;
From field to kiln the wagons go, piled high with bags of hops,
There's bustle in the farmer's house, and in the village shops.

At length the fragrant blooms are safe, the yearly task is o'er,
And on the farms round Ledbury Town, each barn becomes a store
Of pockets, ranged in long straight rows, like soldiers on parade,
The oast-house fires have been withdrawn, the noisy pickers paid.

The city dwellers have returned, to smoke and grime again,
Those faces, pale a month ago, now tanned by sun and rain.
The gypsy vans have headed West, along the road to Wales,
To pitch their camps in wooded dells, before the winter gales.

'Tis quiet now round Ledbury Town, there's peace in Bishop's Froome,
'Tis silent now in barn and byre, and in the farmer's home,
The final act that ends the scene, as daylight hours decline,
Are winking fires in hop yards, where men are burning bine.

Geoffrey Bright, *Hereford is Heaven,* 1948.

CHAPTER 1

The Flavour in the Beer

'For Hops, we make haste to be the chief Hop-masters in England; our Country having store of Coppice-woods, and many provident men within these three years planting abundance of the fairest and largest sort of hops. All about Bromyard in a base (low-lying) soil there is a great store.'

John Beale, 1656.

It is hard to imagine the disruption of normal commercial and social life that only a generation ago would descend on Bromyard and the surrounding countryside for a month each year. September meant one thing – hop picking.

Until the 16th century, England's national drink had been ale – a malted drink flavoured with alecost (costmary), alehoof (ground ivy), wormwood and other substances, but when hops were first used to flavour and preserve ale is unknown. There is evidence that they were cultivated in Bavaria in the 8th century, in the Low Countries in the 10th century, and 400 years later they were being imported into England. 'Strong ale' went out of fashion as the upper classes took to drinking imported wine, and the use of hops may have been encouraged by the need to find a way of flavouring and preserving the weaker 'small beer', which was made from inferior materials and which did not keep as well. 'Small beer' was cheap and therefore popular with the poor, and along with 'small cider' was used in part payment of servants and labourers. Hops were used to preserve 'small cider' made from a second pressing of the apples. Contrary to popular belief, the use of hops in brewing has no effect on the alcoholic content of beer. A dictionary published in London in 1440 gives as its definition of hops, 'sede for beyre', and Arnold's chronicle of 1502 records that beer was first made in London by 'beer brewers strangers, Flemings, Dutchmen', indicating that not only were the hops imported, but also the brewers.

It is often stated that an act was passed in 1424 banning the growing of hops, 'this wicked weed', as they were referred to. There is no evidence of this act in any form, although there certainly was opposition from herbalists and others on economic grounds. The plant has also been used to make coarse brown paper, strong sacking, binders for sheaves of corn, cinnamon-brown dye for wool, and as a substitute for oak bark in tanning.

The hop *(humulus lupulus)* belongs to the same family as hemp and cannabis, and is a relative of the nettle. A hardy, long-lived, climbing perennial, its shoots can reach 20 feet in length but die back to ground level every winter. It has no tendrils and climbs clockwise round its support. Although it will grow in the poorest soils, only optimum

Hops grown on poles and a load ready for drying at Brookhouse Farm, Avenbury, before the First World War. Elsie Cook, the booker, is standing next to her brother Hubert.

Hops ready for picking on wire-work, the modern method of supporting the bines. Brewers use the hop cone with its bract and glands containing various resins and oils.

conditions will produce the quality needed for today's shrinking markets. As a result, hop growing in Herefordshire is now concentrated in the sheltered river valleys of the Frome and Lugg, where there are at least 18 inches of loamy soil with a medium to heavy texture and a good structure for the roots to establish permanent systems. A plentiful supply of water and food is needed for rapid growth and to balance the loss of moisture through the leaves, while good drainage is also essential to aerate the soil and prevent waterlogging. An unusually light rainfall averaging 12 inches between April and September, together with suitable temperatures, produce excellent oil and resin development in local hops. In some areas, the field in which they are grown is called a hop garden, however in Herefordshire it is always known as a hopyard.

By tradition, hops were first grown in England for beer in the 1520s in Kent. The practice soon spread to most other counties, including Herefordshire where the crop has been extensively cultivated in at least 80% of the county's parishes at some period during the last 400 years; in his *Tour* published in 1724 Defoe observed that the inhabitants of Herefordshire were: 'a diligent and laborious people, chiefly addicted to husbandry and they boast, that they have the finest wool, the best hops, and the richest cyder, in all Britain. As for hops they plant in abundance indeed all over the county, and they're very good.'

In the 16th and 17th centuries, hops were planted by inserting three plants, called stocks or setts, around the edges of large holes filled with rich fertile soil and located in rows across the hopyard. During the spring and summer, the surrounding ground was pared of weeds and built up round the setts to form a flat-topped conical mound called a hill. A long pole, usually of ash, chestnut or alder, was sunk in the ground at an angle by each sett so that it leant outwards, while two young shoots were trained up it and tied with a rush. All other shoots were removed from the sett. It was soon found that the weight of hops on the poles caused the wind to break or blow them over, and to help prevent this the poles were tied together at the top with strong twine. Until the discovery of wood preservatives such as creosote, the hop poles only lasted about two years. Thus, replacement of poles was a large, recurring expense, with up to 700 new poles per acre being needed each year, and this continuous demand was the main reason why there were so many ash beds and coppices in hop-growing districts. After the hops had been picked the ground between the hills was dug by hand and manured. A reference to hills occurs in a legal document dated 1638 for the manor of Buttas in King's Pyon, where there was a 'large new frame of buildings wherein there is a dairy house, a kiln house, a store house, six lofts well boarded for malting hop or other use' and a hopyard that 'hath 2000 hills furnished with 6000 poles'.

In the Bromyard district, the first reference to hops appears to be in Swithun Butterfield's survey of 1577 for the bishop of Hereford of the farms in Whitbourne:

'A lytle pcell of land called the hoppyarde lyeth between Brownyng land and Gregory Collins land, cont by estim. 1 rood.'

By 1649 the 'hop-masters' of Bromyard had established the district as one of the main hop-growing areas of the country and the yards at Whitbourne Court 'though uncertain had been known to produce hops to the value of £700.' Hops are still grown in Whitbourne, so they have been cultivated in the parish for well over 400 years.

The *Book of the Farm* (Stephens 1877) lists: 'All the particulars requisite for the furnishing of a new hop ground and the expense per acre attending them is as follows:

	£	s.	d
Draining	6	-	-
Spade and fork tending	7	-	-
Manure, 500 cubic yard at 3s.	7	10	-
Lime, 200 bushels @ 6d. and spreading	5	-	-
Harrowing and rolling		2	-
Setting off 1194 hills, at 6½ feet apart		2	-
Planting 1194 hills of bedded sets, @ 1/2 per 100		14	-
Compost for 1194 hills	1	-	-
3582 bedded plants at 6d. per 100		17	-
Twisting the young bines and repairing the hills in autumn		15	-
	£29	-	-

One man @ 3s., and assistant @ 2s., and 2 boys @ 6d. each, in all 6/-, will set off 3 acres a day. Two men @ 2s. each, and 1 boy @ 6d., in all 4/6 will

Winter work on a farm near Ledbury in 1934. Preparing new poles for the creosote tank.

Hop poles stacked in 'wigwams' for the winter at the Lays Farm, Tarrington.

plant 600 hills a day. In the first year of a new hopground, the soil between the hills may be cropped with a green crop, manured for itself, in order to keep the ground clean, and cause it to make some return for the great outlay incurred in converting it into a hop ground.'

By the end of the 18th century, hops were also being grown on long low ridges spaced six to eight feet apart, running from one side of the hopyard to the other, with the poles placed on the ridge and tied at the top with a string. Midway between the poles a vertical string often hung down from the top string, its lower end anchored into the ground with a special tool. After picking the poles were left in piles on the ground, later to be stacked in 'wigwams' for the winter. Hop poles, as a tenants 'fixture' were often advertised in farm sale particulars – for example *Hereford Journal* 1805: a farm at Clehonger with four hop-kilns was selling 40,000 hop poles with the farm live & dead stock.

Creosote to preserve them became generally available in 1862 and many farms had their long narrow creosote tanks with a fireplace and chimney at one end. The creosote was heated to allow it to soak into the home-grown poles and fencing stakes, which were stood on end, whereas the poles for wirework were laid full length.

Loudon's *Encyclopaedia of Agriculture* of 1835 commented that: 'Wires of copper or iron have been tried as a substitute for wooden poles in the North of France... we do not think it any improvement.'

By the 1850s, nevertheless, because of the high cost of growing hops on poles and with wire already being used extensively for fencing, attempts were also being made in this country to grow hops on permanent wires similar to the espalier system used in fruit growing. This research led to the invention of hop wirework, a firmly anchored framework of posts and wires containing a network of strings reaching from each plant to the top wire up which the shoots could climb. By 1871 several of the larger growers in Herefordshire were using it. The patterns of wirework and stringing have varied from area to area, but all provide a system of wires and strings to support the crop, otherwise the whole row would collapse when the bine is pulled. Polework continued to be used in many smaller yards, for example at Lowdy Hall, Ullingswick, until 1958. Once a hopyard had been established, it would go on producing hops for fifteen years or more without replanting, provided it was properly cultivated and manured, and kept relatively free of disease. When a yard was nearing the end of its useful life, it was common practice to plant fruit trees in the hop rows. The trees were protected from grazing animals until the hops were removed about six years later, when the fruit trees would be large enough to need little protection. To this day, many orchards in the county still show the ridge and furrow of a hopyard with the trees growing on ridges.

In the early 19th century, no hop grower expected to pick a worthwhile crop more than one year in every three. This was because of the ravages of aphids (blight). Various attempts were made to control this damage, such as using smoke from bonfires, spreading foul-smelling dung, and hanging sticky flypapers. Towards the end of the century, it was discovered that a mixture of boiled soft soap and quassia mixed with water and sprayed onto the hop plant would reduce the infestation. This is one of the reasons why at many farmsteads one finds in the back kitchen or amongst the farm buildings very large washboilers or furnaces used to prepare the spray. On the larger hop farms central steam-driven pumping stations were established, the spray being boiled by steam and then pumped through pipes to tanks in the hopyards used to fill the sprayers. The small growers used hand-pumped sprayers or knapsack sprayers, while the larger growers had heavy power sprayers pulled by three horses with the pump being driven from the wheels.

So far, twenty references to hops have been found in the county's wills and inventories up to 1700, and two extracts show the changes in hop-picking techniques that were taking place. The early method of picking hops in Herefordshire was to spread a picking sheet, a blanket or a hessian sheet, on the ground and to pick the hops on to it. Picking sheets are often listed in inventories in the Bromyard district up to the late 17th century, but unlike other areas never picking baskets. From 1700 onwards there are increasing mentions of hop cribs and crib cloths. The first inventory is dated 9 October 1682 and is that of John Norgroves of 'Witbourne', yeoman:

Hops in the house	£6
One old kiln hair, one old sack, one picking sheet, two	
old bags and two pairs of scales	£3 6s. 8d.
400 hop poles	4s.
Hop poles in Richard Lovedale's house	£1

Norgroves used a sheet, but a decade later the second inventory of 23 March 1692 shows that William Toombs of Pencombe, blacksmith, had been picking his hops into a crib:

A small parcel of hops and a stone of wool	14s.	8d
6 Bushels of Lent grain, one old hair cloth, a crib cloth and scales	13s.	

When Thomas Lane of Tipton Hall, Tedstone Delamere, died in 1732, the inventory indicated that he had been making both beer and cider:

'In the Servantemens Room two bedds and a todd of old hopps	£2	0s	0d
In the Back Kitchen two ffurnaces & other Lumber	£2	10s	0d
In the Killhouse two Killhares & One maltmill two Grates and other things there	£2	0s	0d
The Cydermill Screws Hares and all appurtenances thereto	£3	10s	0d
Hogsheads Tubbs Sceels Coopers ware together with the Cider & malt Drink in them	£13	0s	0d

The same year Matthew God of Westwood, Thornbury, dried his crop in a kiln using charcoal, and Herbert Osborn of Stoke Prior died leaving 'In the Brew House a small Brass furnace & Irons & Iron Boiler'.

The cribs, called bins in Kent, were rough wooden frames about 7 feet by 3 feet with hessian sewn on to form containers, and in 1774, Thomas Lewis, maltster, in the Butcher Row, Hereford, (of which only the Old House remains) was advertising 'A quantity of HOP-SACKING of the best sorts'. The men employed as pole pullers moved the cribs up the rows, which were divided into 'houses' to regulate the picking in the yards. The walls of each house were formed by two adjacent rows, and in polework the length consisted of about twenty stocks, while in wirework the crosswires defined the length. In each case all bines within the house had to be picked before the crib was moved into the next one. In polework, the poles were pulled out of the ground and rested on the end of the crib and the bines, which had twisted round and round the poles, had to be cut off before the actual picking could start. In wirework, the bines were cut off about 4 feet above ground and then pulled off the top wire, and dropped into the crib for picking. If a farm had both wirework and polework, the pole hops were often picked at a higher price than the wirework ones as they were disliked by the pickers. Also unpopular were the bad patches of hops into which the farmer's children and their friends often found the house crib moved, lest the regular pickers should feel 'hard done by' and a surprising slowness come upon them at the approach of the offending patch!

The early pickers were the farm labourers' wives and children, and at Hanley, Worcestershire, in 1753, the rate for three weeks work for a woman was 9s. 6d. By 1840

After arriving by train, pickers loading on to a wagon to go to the farm.

piece-work was being advocated at which a good picker could earn 1s. 6d. a day. With the coming of the railways it became popular to import labour from South Wales or the Black Country, attracted not only by the prospect of hop picking but by the chance to stock up with apples for the winter. They came to the nearest railway station in special trains, as many as 2,000 or more arriving in a day at small country stations. Until the opening of the Bromyard line in the 1870s, the Black Country pickers for Whitbourne, Knightwick and Suckley travelled by train as far as Stourport, then made their way to the big yard at the Dog Inn at Dunley and from there were taken by horse drawn wagons to the surrounding farms, often involving long journeys with pickers, children, dogs, luggage, cooking utensils, all piled in together. They were housed in farm buildings, tents, or in flimsy hovels known as barracks. This may be one of the reasons why some hop farms appear to have more buildings with lofts than other farms, these extra so-called tallets having been originally floored as a way of using roof space to house hop pickers.

After the hops had been picked into the crib they had to be measured or bushelled. The busheller called out the count in a loud voice as he measured the green (freshly picked) hops into a sack held by the sack holder. The count was kept by a tally man who carried a quantity of tallies hung on a belt. These were pieces of wood about 15 inches long, split into two pieces, the second piece of the pair being given to the picker. The two pieces would only fit together in a certain position and the count was recorded by file marks across both pieces. By the late 19th century, Herefordshire

Picking polework at Lower Court, Ullingswick, in 1902. Four cribs abreast in their 'houses', with poles resting on the two nearest cribs ready for picking.

Bushelling at Avenbury Court in 1905 – the boy is waiting to mark the tally stick. A bushel, in this case a basket, is a measure of capacity equal to 8 gallons (36 litres) also used for corn and fruit.

growers were using hop checks or tokens which were coin-like discs of brass, iron or zinc, of several sizes, stamped with the grower's name. The smallest represented single bushels which were exchanged for others marked 1, 3, 5, 10 and £1, indicating the amount earned in shillings and pounds. These were counted out to the picker at each bushelling and exchanged for cash at the end of picking. They were later replaced by the booking system. The booker entered the amount in his or her book and in a smaller book retained by the picker. In the evenings there would always be pickers wanting a 'sub' or part-payment for their work. This would entail the return of the checks or it would have to be entered in both the picker's and the master's books, care being taken that the grower always owed the picker some money, otherwise the picker might leave. The rate paid per bushel was agreed between growers and pickers, usually after the first day's picking, and in the 1920s and '30s varied between about 5 bushels to the shilling if hops were big and in good condition, and 2 bushels to the shilling for those that were very small or diseased.

For at least 300 years Herefordshire has grown more hops than the local brewers needed. As Defoe noted in 1724, cider was 'the common drink of the county, and so very good and cheap, that we never found fault, though we could get no other drink for 20 miles together.' Thus few of the hops rushed to the Annual Hop Fairs at Worcester on September 19th and to the Hereford fairs for 'cattle, cheese, hops and linen', are likely to have been for local consumption. Notoriously bad roads, the Wye only navigable with difficulty, no canal until 1845 and no railway until 1853, would have added considerably to the cost of transport, but this was offset to some extent by the fact that the crop could be produced more cheaply in Herefordshire than in other parts of the country. The demand was there, however, helped by government propaganda in favour of beer drinking instead of gin. With the expansion of the towns, breweries were established all over the country, and some years a million barrels of beer were produced in London and the suburbs alone. Between 1880 and the 1920s, Ledbury, Leominster and Tenbury each had several small breweries registered, although Bromyard appears to have had none. Many farmers secured their markets by direct contracts with West Midland brewers who preferred the high quality, less coarse varieties grown locally. One such grower was Perry Pudge of New House, Bishops Frome, who took pockets of hops, known as 'Pudges', to the Black Country before the First World War and sold them individually to small breweries there.

There are numerous references to hops in the *Hereford Journal*. For instance, in October 1770: 'At our fair, on Saturday last, hops sold from £4. 4s. to £6. And on Monday hops advanced considerably.' The same month storage space was being offered: 'HOPS may stand, on very reasonable Terms, in a large and commodious Room, which will be always ready for their Reception during the Season, at the Red-Streak-Tree Inn, in this City.' In November a Mr George inadvertently found himself providing unplanned warehouse room: '*WHEREAS* at *HEREFORD FAIR* on Saturday the 20th inst. a *POCKET* of *HOPS* was sent away, by Mistake, with other Hops, the Property of Mr Philip George of Worcester: Whoever can prove it to be their Property (by applying to Mr George) may have it again, paying for Costs and Charges.' Then on 17 September 1851 there was an appeal that:

'Whenever we have a railway into this city, immediate steps must be taken for establishing a hop market, here, in order that the farmers may dispose of Hereford hops in their own county, and not have the trouble of journeying to

MAP 1 – THE BROMYARD DISTRICT OF HEREFORDSHIRE
with railways serving the locality.

The hopyard at Lower Court, Ullingswick, again. There is a wealth of detail in this photograph with the poles, a milk can and lunch baskets in the shade of the rigid Herefordshire crib, the large old kitchen knife stuck in the corner post, the sacking aprons and the cotton sun bonnets. A small brother minds the toddler whilst his older sisters help their mother pick.

a distant market to sell what may be disposed of at their own doors – great part of the hops of Herefordshire being disposed of at Worcester, acquire the title of "Worcester hops" and thus rob us of the celebrity of our own county's growth.'

Six years later the plea had been partially heeded with the building of the Corn Exchange in Broad Street where the corn merchants also held a hop market, and in season the smell of hops permeated Broad Street from a hop warehouse next to the Exchange. Although the first railway lines had reached Hereford in 1853, Slater's Directory of 1859 states that cider, grain, hops and oak bark were still being 'conveyed down the Wye, and by the canal to Gloucester and other places.' The next year the Worcester/Hereford line was opened and barge traffic began to decline. The Corn Exchange was converted into the Kemble Theatre in 1911, but it continued to be used as a corn exchange on Wednesdays when there would be no matinees. The theatre had a sliding roof which could be opened on hot summer nights and to clear the atmosphere between performances. The corn exchange ceased operating in 1950 and the theatre was demolished in 1963. There were other markets such as those at

Chelmsford and Salisbury, but the largest was the Borough Market in London, and when the telephone exchange for the Borough High Street was built it was called Hopmarket.

Home brewing of beer would have created a need for small quantities of hops. A household guide of c1800, *The Young Woman's Companion or Female Instructor*, assured its readers that an excellent table beer fit for drinking in three or four weeks could be made from 3 bushels of malt, yeast, 39 gallons of water and 1½ pounds of hops. During the Napoleonic wars, however, the rise in the price of malting barley and hops made home brewing too expensive for poorer households and beer was largely replaced by tea in the home, with a visit to the public house for any beer drinking. In 1851 four innkeepers in Bromyard were still doing their own brewing and malting. The practice which had started in the 18th century of farmers paying their labourers' wages partly in beer or cider, was understandably frowned on by the Temperance Movement, and home-brewed beer rapidly disappeared from farmhouses after 1880 when a duty was imposed on beer. The Truck Acts of 1887 and 1896 made the daily cider allowance in lieu of wages illegal, but it was so popular with their labourers that it was continued by many local farmers as a free issue.

Hops have always proved an erratic source of income. Disease, pests, taxes and the weather made fluctuations in yields and profits such a regular feature of the 18th century that betting on the rate of hop duty was a popular pastime at Worcester market. The first half of the 19th century saw the highest acreage of hops ever planted in the Bromyard district with 4,251 acres in 1835, but overproduction, blight and foreign competition, led to a drop of 65% by 1860. A gradual rise then occurred until, in 1900, the figure was back to 2,050 acres, about half the peak acreage of 1835. By the First World War, foreign dumping had caused a drop of 45 %, since when there has been a slow but steady contraction to about 650 acres in 1985.

Eighteenth-century writers also depict the uncertain nature of hop growing. In 1729, Richard Bradley, a professor of botany at Cambridge, wrote that ground previously worth less than a shilling an acre was now fetching up to £50 a year if planted with hops. By 1793, however, Nathaniel Kent, who knew the Tenbury district well, was complaining in his *Hints to Gentlemen of Landed Property* that hop growing in Hereford and Worcester was not in the long-term interests of landowners, as tenants were keeping most of the farmyard manure for their hops and sacrificing good pasture for alder beds to supply hop poles. Fifteen years later *The Leominster Guide*, while remarking on the size of the local hop grounds and how some farmers had managed to buy the farms they had previously rented, continued that great profits no longer existed owing to overproduction, heavy duties, and the brewers finding substitutes.

Ale, beer and hops had long been targets for taxation; the last item in the Domesday list of Herefordshire customs records that, 'Any man's wife who brewed ale inside or outside the City gave 10d as a customary due.' As with all agricultural produce since earliest times, farmers paid tithe on their hops and in 1835 Loudon explained that: 'When tythe of hops is taken in kind the parson may either take every tenth basket

A group of pickers and visitors at Thornbury Court in 1914.

when green or every tenth sack when dried in the latter case allowing 25s. per cwt for drying, sacking and duty.' A good source of information on hop growing that can be used in any county are the tithe maps and apportionments prepared as a result of the Tithe Commutation Act of 1836. This abolished the payment of tithe in kind, where it still existed, and substituted a money rent instead. As hops were assessed separately, it is possible to discover which farmers were growing them in which fields. For example, in 1841 a third of all the farms and smallholdings in Little Cowarne had a hopyard however small; of the 693 acres in the parish 50 acres were devoted to hops. A year later in the adjacent parish of Stoke Lacy (2,584 acres), just over a quarter of the 88 farms and smallholdings had hopyards ranging in size from ½ – 6½ acres, with three quarters of the crop being produced on the 7 largest farms. Field names, such as the Old Hop Yard, often indicate farms which had grown hops in the past, but were no longer doing so by the date of the apportionment; evidence of hop growing has been found in 207 of the 250 or so parishes of Herefordshire.

In addition to tithe, hop farmers paid an excise duty, and 1711 saw the introduction of hop duty. The excise list at the British Library for the years 1807-1861 shows that for many years Herefordshire was growing over 10,000 acres or nearly a quarter of the total crop. The excise officers had to be notified when picking was due to start, so that they could supervise the drying, weighing and packing of the hops, and on

3 September 1851 the *Hereford Journal* reported that, 'The excisemen have commenced their rounds.'

Two seasons of low prices in 1821 and 1822 had caused hardship, and an urn was presented to John Walker, the great-great-great-grandfather of Peter Walker of Ankerdine, Knightwick, for his 'unwearied exertions in assisting to obtain a remission of part of the Hop Duty for the year 1822'; and in 1849 a deputation to the chancellor of the exchequer tried to delay the collection of the duty due in October. A further deputation from all the hop growing districts in March 1862 urged the chancellor to abolish both hop duty and excise duty and later that year they were repealed. The same year import duty was removed, but in spite of foreign competition the national acreage planted increased until 1878 when it was 71,789 acres, the highest recorded.

Four years later there was a devastating attack of aphids, and the total yield dropped from the 455,000 cwt of 1881 to only 120,000 cwt, and the price of hops increased threefold from approximately £5 to £15 per cwt. Only four years on again, in 1886, there was a bumper crop when extra accommodation had to be found for the pockets

Soldiers from Froome Bank Convalescent Home, Bromyard, picking at Little Froome during the First World War.

of hops in Worcester at the Skating Rink, the old Exhibition Building, the Guildhall and the Shirehall.

By 1905 the picture was not so satisfactory and on 7 September the *Bromyard News and Record* reported that, in his evidence to the Agricultural Committee of the Tariff Commission, the well-known hop factor, Mr Edward Le May, brought out clearly the economic advantages to this country that would flow from a revival of the hop industry, which had declined in acreage by a third since 1878. A week later, the paper returned to the subject of hops:

> 'The wet weather must have been of great discomfort to pickers, for nearly every day in the past fortnight it has rained, and at times very heavily too. Prices offered for good samples the last two Saturdays have been very disheartening and many a grower came back last week with the determination of having "no more". There is not much prospect of prices improving either, especially when the foreign berries arrive in England – free of duty. '

The industry was in a depressed state and numerous meetings were held to protest against the dumping of foreign hops and to campaign for an import duty. Imports had been building up since the 1850s, and by 1900 had reached as many as 150,000 cwt from the USA, 35,000 cwt from Belgium and 12,000 cwt from Germany. T. Lawson Walker of Knightwick Manor helped organise a mass meeting of growers and pickers in London on 16 May 1908, Hop Saturday, and he was one of the speakers at the meeting in Trafalgar Square. Berrow's *Worcester Journal* described how:

> 'Early in the day local growers, accompanied by bands of labourers, wended their way to the various stations on the Hereford and Leominster lines to join the special trains. Nearly 400 travelled by the special on the Leominster line and 500 to 600 by the Hereford train. The two contingents met at Shrub Hill. Those travelling from the Tenbury district, together with a large company of pickers from the Black Country proceeded via Birmingham and Oxford. Local growers took numbers of their own men with them and paid their fares... More than 50,000 marched in procession to Trafalgar Square.'

It was said that many Herefordshire growers, with those from other areas, did not get any further than the first pub near Paddington Station! They did at least have a good day out, but the government of the day took no action to improve the situation and by 1914 the pressure of continuing imports caused a further national decline of over 2,000 acres.

This account of aspects of hop growing prior to the First World War sets the scene for the earliest photographs and recollections, before setting the local industry in its national context.

After the removal of hop duty in 1862, the national hop area expanded to a peak in 1878 as new growers were attracted to the crop, especially in the South East (see Graph 1 on p.175). Many lacked capital, farmed in marginal locations, and grew coarser varieties, and competition from imported hops caused severe decline, speedier in the South East than in the West Midlands. Between 1878 and 1918, the West Midlands lost 56% of hop acreage; Kent & Sussex lost 81%. In the last decade of the 19th century, the acreage in the West Midlands actually increased, both in Worcestershire's Teme valley and around Bromyard, mainly in the lower Frome valley, while the acreages in more upland parishes continued to decline.

The West Midlands' share of the national area began to increase in the latter part of the 19th century, as growers adopted quality 'aroma' hops earlier and paid closer attention to cultivation and drying.

It was said in 1864 that hops in Worcestershire and Herefordshire were picked far more free of leaves than in Kent. Costs were lower and, as land was cheaper, rows could be more widely spaced, allowing the use of horse cultivations as early as the 1790s. Growers were more progressive, introducing several innovations during the 1860s and 1870s. Creosote tanks to preserve hop poles were in use in the West Midlands in the 1860s, doubling the life of poles. Wider rows encouraged the adoption of wirework, and enabled the earlier use of horse-drawn spraying machines. Forced draught, too, was being tried in Worcestershire in the early 1870s, using steam-driven fans.

The growth of industry in South Wales, Birmingham and the Black Country created huge demand for beer, where local growers maintained direct contracts with brewers. Good rail communications not only eased the transport of hops and beer, but also tapped a willing pool of hop pickers.

Herefordshire's preference for square kilns [see Chapter 8] proved an advantage in the 20th century, allowing the conversion of existing kilns to two-tier drying or the installation of roller hairs. Hop yards in the South East suffered earlier and more severely from verticillium wilt, partly due to growing more susceptible varieties.

In the 20th century, West Midlands growers continued to innovate more rapidly than the South East, developing and adopting picking machines earlier.

Table 1. Percentage of hops (by pockets) picked by machine.

Year	South East	West Midlands	% of Total
1954	7	39	17
1957	34	78	49

Source: A. H. Burgess, p.193.

From the 1970s the rise in lager consumption promoted a switch to 'high alpha' varieties, prompting some growers to leave the industry. However, recent revival of interest in real ales has benefited the West Midlands, where 'aroma' hops have always been more important than in the South East. By 2005, the region had overtaken the South East.

Hop growing parishes in the West Midlands in 1861.

Source: *British Parliamentary Papers 1862 LV*

©Joan Grundy 2007

Map 2. All parishes in the West Midlands region growing more than 8 ha of hops are within Herefordshire (62), Worcestershire (24) and Shropshire (1). Mapping these parishes emphasises the strikingly localised distribution of the industry between the rivers Severn and Wye. The core area lies in the lower Frome and the Teme valleys, where there are exceptionally deep, free draining alluvial soils. Hop yards remain prominent in the same districts in 2007.

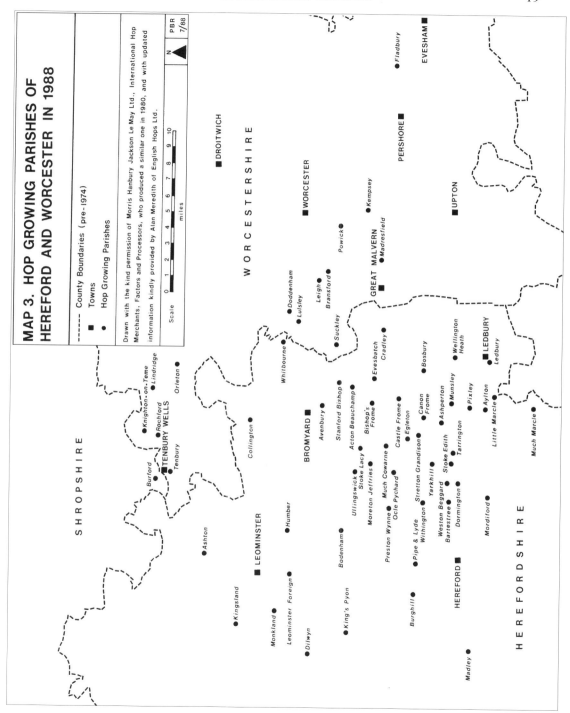

MAP 3. HOP GROWING PARISHES OF HEREFORD AND WORCESTER IN 1988

- - - - - County Boundaries (pre-1974)
■ Towns
● Hop Growing Parishes

Drawn with the kind permission of Morris Hanbury Jackson Le May Ltd., International Hop Merchants, Factors and Processors, who produced a similar one in 1980, and with updated information kindly provided by Alan Meredith of English Hops Ltd.

Scale 0 1 2 3 4 5 6 7 8 9 10
miles

N

PBR
7/88

CHAPTER 2

A View from the Farmhouse

'Whome fancie persuadeth, among other crops,
to have for his spending, sufficient of hops…'

Thomas Tusser 1524?-1580.

During hop picking the usual pattern of life was disturbed for the whole area. Bromyard became a ghost town with nothing stirring – except on a Saturday afternoon. No public functions were held and nothing could be done until 'after hop picking'. Hop farmers and their families remained at home except for essential business and shopping, and meals were fitted in to suit bushelling and kiln changes.

At the turn of the century, the Eckleys lived at Church House, Pencombe, where

Hop picking at Munderfield Court in 1909. *L to R:* Three Dudley pickers, Edith Passey, Kate Eckley, William Ingram (polepuller), Mrs. Ingram, Annie Vernalls, William Nottingham (polepuller), and a Dudley picker. *In front:* ? and Jimmy Eckley.

the hops were grown up poles, and Mrs Eckley, who was more interested than her husband in the crop, did the tying before the birth of her daughter in 1899. When they moved to Munderfield Court, Avenbury, there were local pickers and others from Dudley; on arrival the latter, taking their own plates, collected a hot meal of roast beef and vegetables from the farmhouse. Their sleeping quarters were over the cow shed with a kitchen nearby in a wainhouse where there was a fireplace for cooking. The one man among the pickers had his own 'bedroom' curtained off at the end of the sleeping quarters and he went to bed first.

In the evenings the pickers entertained themselves. They were all great dancers; one of them, Sarah Anne, who was also a good singer, did the cakewalk to the delight of the Eckley children. In contrast, knowing Mr Eckley was considered a religious man, there was nightly hymn-singing ending with the pickers standing outside the farmhouse to sing, 'Lead, Kindly Light'. Many of the women sold their crochet work locally. When the pickers went home, the boxes of provisions they had brought with them were full of apples and other fruits to which they had helped themselves. At Christmas Mrs Eckley always sent a turkey to Dudley for her pickers.

Of all the local villages, it was Bishops Frome which saw the greatest influx of pickers and a whole town would develop there. In the years before the First World War and during the '20s and '30s, the population of about 700 increased to 5,000 or

A peaceful view of the Chase Inn, Bishops Frome, about 1910, with the Green Dragon in the background.

more, largely because of the hop-growing empire built up by William Farmer Pudge, born at New House, Bishops Frome, in 1851. Pudges had long been connected with Bishops Frome, but it was Farmer Pudge, a shrewd businessman, who turned from running the Chase Inn and a butcher's shop to concentrate on hops, and in the 1880s and 1890s bought Upper House, Walton and the Court specifically for the purpose. During the First World War he grew wheat, but planted up with hops again when peace returned. Between the Wars, he was said to be the largest private hop grower in England with over 200 acres of hops in Bishops Frome, together with many other hop farms in the area. 'It was just like looking at a sea of hops off the top of Fromes Hill,' says Gilbert Hyde. Busloads came on outings from Wales to walk the yards just before picking, and Pudge is reputed to have offered a shilling to anyone who could find a weed. When asked what he put on his hops, he would only divulge that it was 'the best, the best!' After a fire which gutted the hop kilns at the Court in 1926, he salvaged the red bricks from the service quarters at Cowarne Court and built a massive new drying complex at Upper House, behind the Chase Inn, with twelve 20 foot kilns under one roof, the largest in the country.

Farmer Pudge died in 1938 and his only daughter, Mrs Woodward, continued the business until it was wound up about 1962, when the drying complex behind the Chase Inn was relegated to a warehouse. These buildings have now been replaced by houses, but Pudges are still growing hops at the New House, Frogend, Moorend and Bromtrees Hall.

Pudge imported all his pickers. Those from South Wales were accommodated on Upper House Farm in various sheds and barracks known as 'Tin Town'; while in fields on the back road to Burley Gate near the Filly Brook, there would be row upon row of caravans. In one field those belonging to the gypsies, the real Romanies, and in another, those of the didicoys or 'hedgecrawlers' (a Herefordshire word for tinkers). Gilbert Bowler remembers: 'It was a grand sight to see the gypsies arriving in their caravans with the dogs tied to the back axles, and horses and foals running behind.' And Edith Silcock knew them as 'tidy, respectable people who did not mix much with the other pickers. They might snare a few rabbits, but they were an honest lot, the troublemakers "coming from away". If any of the gypsy girls, and they were very pretty, strayed from their cribs one of their men-folk soon rounded them up and brought them back. They always had a number of horses and ponies with them, and on Sundays horse dealing would go on outside the Chase Inn, the men running up and down the road to show off the good points of their animals.' Wads of money were seen to change hands, always going to the head of the family. Every year a butcher from the Butter Market in Hereford used to set up a stall in Bishops Frome and he is still remembered for his call, 'If you wants to buy some meat, buy some meat, if not move the baby's ass off the slab!' The *Bromyard News and Record* of 1 October 1931 carried an end of season report: 'Round Bishops Frome the yards are denuded, but in "camp town" near the Roman Catholic Church there are still many residents, the children of whom – of which there were many without stockings or boots – seem to hop about most cheerfully in spite of the thorns and brambles.'

Aerial view of Upper House kilns, Bishops Frome.

View of Upper House kilns from bank above Bishops Frome.

Rev. Jane Davies

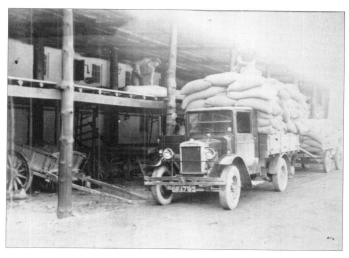

Upper House, Bishops Frome. Unloading sacks on to the greenstage.

Farmer Pudge, Upper House, Bishops Frome.

Upper House, Bishops Frome. The press in the hop room with kiln hairs full of hops waiting to be bagged in the background.

Gypsy encampment with cooking pots hung over the fire.

Hops had been grown for many years at Instone Court, Bishops Frome, when the farm was bought in 1920 by Sidney Parker; his family had been hop growers for many generations and there are still five Parkers in the area maintaining the tradition. At Instone cartsheds and wainhouses were used as eating places for the imported pickers. Planks and doors placed on empty drums served as tables and although benches were provided some preferred to sit on large blocks of wood. Each family had an allotted space arranged by the ganger woman and most had pieces of American oil cloth or newspaper for a tablecloth. For sleeping, haylofts, pigsties, cattle pens, etc, were cleaned up and partitions made for families by hanging hessian from the beams to meet the low wooden divisions of the range of pigsties. Boltings of straw were used to make beds. Blankets and hessian sheets were issued on the day of arrival, to be returned on leaving and all were washed as soon as possible afterwards. At the beginning of the next season they were put on the kilns for airing and this also served as a trial run for the kilns themselves. Premises had to be whitewashed and seen by the Sanitary Inspector before they were occupied, and latrines provided.

Fires were a frequent hazard on hop farms and must have been grim with no telephones and only horse-drawn fire engines. Sidney Parker, who had a horror of fire after experiencing one started by a hurricane lamp in a cowshed, would only allow one coke devil for cooking; however, his pickers also had the use of open fires with properly built chimneys, faggots made up during the winter providing the fuel. Before electricity, hurricane lamps were used – dozens of them. Each morning they were brought up to the house for refilling, the job of the unfortunate 'boy'. Farms in the area were not connected to mains electricity until after the Second World War; however, many generated their own supply by installing a dynamo and making use of the stationary engine which was used to drive the fan for the hop kilns. The house at Instone Court was wired for lighting during the 1920s, but with only 50v direct current its use was very limited. In the '30s, a set of storage batteries was obtained which gave greater scope and no time was lost in wiring the hop pickers' quarters – for safety reasons as much as anything else. After the Second World War ex-Army equipment proved very suitable. A large Nissen hut with a cast iron cooker and folding tables and benches were used for the dining room, and other Nissen huts with brick partitions were occupied as sleeping quarters.

Tramps just turned up at Instone, often pushing a pram containing their worldly possessions. They moved from one workhouse to another, occasionally taking on casual work, and were known as 'Milestone Inspectors'. They had to be housed separately from the other pickers and led a very private life of their own. They were not usually very good pickers but managed to earn some money during the season which helped them on their way. They used to lodge small sums with the landlord of the Holly Bush for future use.

On arrival at Cradley Hall Farm, the Dudley pickers were provided with tea and buns by Ethel Paske: 'The tea made in the coal-fired copper in which I did my family washing – I wonder now how I got rid of the taste of soap!' At Instone, a milk churn full of tea was taken down from the house in a donkey cart for breakfast in the hopyard at 9 a.m., and at the first measuring faggots were provided for the pickers to make fires to boil their kettles. The last measuring was usually about 5 p.m. The Parkers ran a shop at the house which sold eggs, butter and home-made cakes when available, rabbits caught on the farm 6d each, and skim milk at 1d a pint. Containers for the milk varied – billycans, jugs, and bottles which were almost impossible to keep clean and which smelt worse and worse as the season progressed. The waste was terrible, particularly bread, and kept the pigs going throughout hop picking with very little extra feeding.

The farmer's wife looked after not only the pickers, but also the key men of the harvest, the driers, with their twenty-four hour job. At Little Froome three men worked in the kilns, and they were provided with four meat meals a day and a middle night feed of meat, pickles, butter, cheese and so on. At Instone Court the driers ate in the house for breakfast, dinner, tea and supper, and were supplied with sandwiches and tea-making equipment for the night. On one occasion instead of sugar in a honey jar Epsom salts in a similar jar were sent in by mistake with a disastrous effect on the driers as they had been adding more and more in a vain attempt to sweeten their tea!

With the war came food rationing, making more work for the farmer's wife and family; the pickers, imported and local, were entitled to extra rations at agricultural rates. 'This was a great thing and a lump of cheese doled out into one's crib on Monday morning was borne home later in triumph, for the ordinary weekly cheese ration was not more than 2 oz,' remembers Mildred Shepherd. On outlying farms away from shops, such as Knightwick Manor and Lower Tedney, the government allowed groceries to be delivered in bulk and the farmers' wives had to weigh up the rations for the pickers – a gargantuan task. At Little Froome, however, Ethel Paske's grocer was very good about doing up and delivering the small portions of butter or margarine, sugar, cheese, tea and jam, for the 150 or so local pickers. Each week they came up to the house for the rations and she took the money. The same thing happened at Instone Court where the ration books of the imported pickers were handed to the grocers. The pickers wrote their orders and Burtons put them up to be distributed by the farm shop, likewise the butcher. Bread was delivered three times a week but pickers did not like it after the first day; however, if it was warmed up in the Aga they were happy. One picker lived next door to a bakery and was used to new bread for every meal.

The declaration of war in 1939 had made many of the pickers from South Wales and the Black Country afraid to leave their homes, fearing they would be bombed. So there was a shortage of pickers and the picking dragged on into October. To help out, some of the men and N.C.O.s of the local company of the Territorial Army were sent along each day but, as may be imagined, they regarded this as a pleasant holiday and not many hops got picked. The same season, preparatory to the issue of Identity Cards, a list had to be compiled of the dates of birth and full names of all the imported pickers and their children, many of whom were very vague about these details. Later on in the war, there was a cosmopolitan crowd on a farm at Burley Gate with two German prisoners of war, and one side of the farm for English people and the other side for the Welsh. On Saturday nights they all sang and the Welsh and the prisoners played accordions.

'Booking was a pleasant job, particularly in good weather', writes Edith Silcock who worked as a booker in Bishops Frome. 'In wet weather it was not so easy, slipping about in deep mud with rainwater dripping off the bines and trying to hold up an umbrella to keep the rain off the book and cards. After the last bushelling of the day those who had run out of funds would come along for a "sub" and draw a pound or two to keep them going, this too being entered on their card and in the book.

The evening after the yards had been cleared and picking finished was hectic for the booker. The number of bushels entered in the book had to be totalled up for each picker and the amount due calculated. This was far from simple as the price for picking at the start usually changed over the weeks so that one would have to calculate say 157 bushels at seven to the shilling, 97 at six to the shilling and 137 at six and a half to the shilling. After working out a hundred or so similar problems one's head became a little muzzy. And all this before the days of pocket calculators! The only help to hand was a well

Edith Silcock booking at Perry Pudge's, the New House, Bishops Frome, in 1939. Cpl. Wells and other Bromyard Territorials were drafted in to help with the crop when there was a shortage of regular pickers.

thumbed ready reckoner. Then the subs had to be totalled and subtracted and in some cases this total was almost as much as the amount earned and there was little to take home.

The following morning the money for paying the pickers had to be fetched from the bank in Worcester. Permission was obtained from the police to park outside the bank and a constable would be on hand while the money was loaded into the car. It amounted to several thousands of pounds, quite a lot of it in silver or copper, so was quite heavy to handle.

Then there was the paying out. A table was set up and the farmer and booker presided at this while each card holder came up in turn, produced their card, the amount due to them was looked up in the book and the farmer counted out their money. When all had been paid they loaded themselves and their belongings into the buses sent for them and set off back to their homes in South Wales. Everyone relaxed, breathed a sigh of relief and another hop picking was over!'

On some farms strikes for more money seemed to occur every year, but never lasted long. At Little Froome, Thursdays were particularly prone to strikes, as Bromyard Market was close at hand and there were bargains to be had. At Instone Court there used to be a ritual confrontation with Sidney Parker which would start noisily but usually end with jokes and laughing and a visit to 'The Tiddly', the Holly Bush: drinks all round on the 'Gaffer' and, weather permitting, the pickers would be back at work the next day. Sometimes the strike went on for another twenty-four hours but this was rare. Very often a rise in the picking rate was obtained – but not always. During the war Mildred Shepherd picked approximately two bushels for a shilling and 'any farmer who gave less was liable to have a strike on his hands.'

Margaret Dallow recalls that gypsies helped with the hops at Garford, Yarkhill, in the early '50s:

'There were thirty-five acres of hops (that is hop acres – 1000 stocks to a hop acre). There would be thirty-six caravans and about forty horses, however after a bit of horse trading and when the lights of the farmhouse had gone out, twenty or thirty more horses might appear. In the morning they would hotly deny there were any extra! One day Granny Smith arrived, two thin plaits looped about her ears and her skirt to the ground, and asked if she could bring her family to work in the hopyards. She had four sons with names like Geldin and Jobie and three daughters. The young women, all with good figures, often had a baby on one arm enveloped in a blanket, leaving the other free to work. They would work very hard at the hop tying, etc, the whole family taking part and doing two fields to the one of the Welsh, but when the time came for them to go to Evesham they would leave. In the middle of August they would return to help finish the harvest and make ready for hop picking. In September their numbers would be swollen with pickers from the Welsh valleys, 200 adults and nearly 100 children, and on a Sunday evening the singing from the covered

September 1944 at Lower Court, Ullingswick. *L to R:* Tom Hamer, Frank Hall, Gwen Brookes, Pini Antonia, Biagio Chibelli, Antonio Bassi, Bert Brookes and Hilda Hamer. The three Italians, from No. 2 P.O.W. Hostel on the Leominster road, came daily to work on the farm.

Bushelling at Little Froome. Flo Preece booking, Adam Jones bushelling and Leonard Lock holding the sack already half full. Ada Powell at the far end of the crib.

Booking in the rain at Upper Lyde.

cowshed was beautiful. The gypsies held the "Master", as they called my father, in great respect and if he went out the gypsy women would patrol the farmhouse to see that my mother and sister and I were all right.'

As a lively conclusion to the old days, Ethel Paske recalls an incident when, owing to the decrease in the local labour force, more gypsies were also being employed at Little Froome: 'On one occasion someone from Highwell House (which overlooks the farm) rang the police to say that murder was being committed at Little Froome. Because my husband was ill I met the police when they arrived and went with them to the gypsies' caravans. The police put the troublemakers into their caravans and I stood watching, couldn't do anything else, for as fast as they were put in at the front they got out at the back!'

Change was taking place by the 1950s, however, and the number of pickers began to dwindle. The war had brought about an increase in regular employment for women, and the local education authorities in the Black Country and Herefordshire, once so co-operative, ruled that their school terms and holidays should be the same as the rest of the country. When picking by hand finally came to an end in the district, about 1970 at Avenbury Court, there were many, nevertheless, who sorely missed the opportunity of working in the hopyards.

Miss Walton and May with a half-end folding crib.

Collecting cribs from the yard at Knightwick Manor and carrying them out to the hop yard, the first day.

CHAPTER 3

'They was Lovely Days'

'In the week all Bromyard went down to Little Froome and Avenbury
Court at six or seven o'clock in the morning out across the fields.'

Layton Edwards, 1985.

As the year begins to turn into Autumn and there is a certain misty freshness in the morning air with the promise of warmth later on, local people still say, 'It's a real hop-picking morning.' They seem to sniff the air and nod in agreement that whatever they are about to do they would much rather be setting off to the hopyard for a day's hop picking, as they would have done thirty or forty years ago.

The majority of the pickers were women and children, in most cases setting out to earn a much welcomed supplement to the family income; a winter coat, a shedful of coal, new furniture or the school uniform for a scholarship child. How the mothers enjoyed this money, particularly because it was theirs to spend as they wished on their own special security or luxury. For three or four weeks all household chores laid aside, they set out with their macs and stools, sandwich boxes and old kitchen knives to take up residence in the hopyard houses, in a different community bound by strict rules enforced by the pole-pullers and a timetable dictated by the busheller and the drying kilns.

Hop picking meant getting up early in the morning to go and meet the lorry at the end of the road or to take the long walk to Paskes at Little Froome. Everyone wore old clothes with long sleeves and trousers or thick stockings to prevent the bines from scratching and scarring bare arms and legs. These clothes held the scent of the hops until the season came round again. An old pram or pushchair was essential equipment for the little ones and the day's supplies. Also needed were extra coats in case of rain and an umbrella, the tin biscuit box with scones or cake for 'bait time' and sandwiches for dinner (not forgetting a damp cloth to clean the worst of the stains from your hands before eating), and tea, sugar and lemonade crystals for the children. Milk and drinking water could be fetched from the farm but the Thermos was filled for the first warm drink of the day before any fires were lit to boil the big black kettles. In case of cuts and scratches there would be some Elastoplast or a bandage with lint, and the washing blue bag in a damp piece of muslin to ease the pain of wasp stings.

Good hop-picking stools were made locally, some by Ernie (Jim) Dallow at Sirrells the blacksmiths. They were all tall enough to enable the picker to sit well up to the crib and had a ledge on which to rest the feet and help to stop the legs of the stool

Arthur Berry, a baker at Weale & Bateman, taking his holiday to pick hops with Elsie and the family.

Mary Pearson booking, Adam Jones bushelling and David Paske holding a greensack at Little Froome.

sinking into the soil. A short-bladed kitchen knife was stuck in the end post of the crib for slicing the bines before pulling them from the overhead wire and cutting them into manageable pieces in the crib.

Older, retired men or those able to take their holidays helped to make up the numbers. A family would have one or two cribs, but a woman on her own would share a half-end with a friend or neighbour. It was important to pick fast enough to keep up with everyone else when the cribs were moved up the yard as each house was cleared.

On the first day, with crib allocated and set out in the dense greenery of the fresh hopyard, voices were muffled and you could not see who was around you, but as the bines were pulled your neighbours came gradually into view to be hailed and greeted as if encountered in a foreign land. The firm hops gradually covered the hessian of the crib and grew into a bright mound until the warning, 'Clear 'em up', came from the busheller and heralded his approach. No leaves, dirt or pieces of bine must remain in the crib when the busheller, bin men and the booker arrived. Measured into

NOTICE.

Pickers are responsible for the loss of this Book and all money due thereon will be paid to bearer only.

1. Any person accepting this book and proceeding to pick shall be deemed to have agreed to and be bound by the undermentioned rules.

2. The hops must be picked clean and free from bine and leaves, and unless so picked they will be removed from the cribs without being measured, and the pickers will not be entitled to be paid for picking them.

3. The employer shall (in addition to all other rights) have the right of discharging any picker or pickers for bad picking or refusing to clean up the cribs for measuring, or to pick up loose hops when required, or who are guilty of any misconduct or interference with other pickers, or who are found smoking in Rickyard or Farm buildings.

4. Pickers dismissed for misconduct, or refusing to remain throughout the whole of the picking, to be paid at the rate of Six Baskets to the shilling, and to forfeit any allowances.

5. The employer to have full power to engage any fresh pickers he may require during the progress of the picking.

☞ Take notice that all persons guilty of taking away poles, fruit, or of any illegal act, will be prosecuted.

TILLEY'S

Hop-Picker's Account Book.

No of Crib_____

Name of Picker _____

_____

No. at Crib_____

MANUFACTURED BY

TILLEY & SON,

Printers & Stationers,

LEDBURY.

Hop-Pickers Account Book.

the sacks, bushelled 'light' or 'heavy' the hops were cleared to a last half measure, your bin card with your number on the front and the rules on the back recorded the morning's picking and it was bait time ... but not for long ... the hungry kilns were awaiting your labours, cut, pull, spray and pick again.

As the house was picked you emerged into the open world where voices were clearer and the cart with the sacks could be seen. Also visible were the pole-pullers crossing the mounds with their long handled tools, taking down the flags – those few sprays left waving on the wire – and turning over the piles of picked bines in case hops were dropped or wasted. Mothers in old raincoats and felt hats or wraparound aprons called to collect up their brood and encourage or bribe them to pick another few boxes or umbrellas full before the busheller came round again. When every bine was cleared it was time to plunge once again into the dense green of a new house, the pole-pullers carrying the crib and all of us trailing behind with our paraphernalia.

After dinner some children would play or go to fetch dry sticks to replenish the fire. Blackberries, and nuts ripening in the hedgerows, mushrooms and windfall apples or pears were all fair game if no damage was done to the trees. It was considered lucky if you found a 'silver grub', the chrysalis of a moth or butterfly hidden on the underside of a leaf, to be taken home in a jam jar and kept in the hope that it might hatch.

The farmyard and buildings were forbidden territory and certain quiet areas behind hedges were designated to provide for 'nature's needs' where a plentiful supply of dock leaves was considered a necessity.

After the last of the day's bushellings the trek home began and many a local father had cooked the tea for the pickers' return. The corner shops were busy and stayed open especially late with supplies of sausages, bacon, cheese and corned beef ready for the next day's bait.

Preparing to load green sacks from the Big Yard at Ankerdine. *R to L:* Alan Morris, 'Captain', 'Polly Perkins' and another.

And so down to work!

It is hard to describe the special atmosphere or camaraderie of the individual hopyards – a sense of belonging to a group with certain customs of their own. The pole-pullers had a certain status, at once authoritarian yet familiar, and as the last bines were pulled a particular custom called cribbing was observed. This was when the unmarried girls were ceremoniously 'dumped' into the crib. Who was chosen, or how, one never knew but sounds of a scuffle and cries of protest would be heard as the unsuspecting girl would be approached from each side, usually by the pole-pullers or binmen, lifted into the air and dropped into the few hops left in the crib. Her shrieks and cries would be accompanied by cheers and laughter as the ancient rite was fulfilled. Sometimes the girls got together and up-ended the bin man in a crib. Another custom was to cure a few whole bines in the kiln to be used at harvest festival and also to decorate the bar at the local pub.

Hop pillows were a favourite remedy for insomnia as the heady scent of the dried hops was claimed to be sleep-inducing.

Sunday was a different day in the hopyard – a late start and always lots of visitors. This was the day many of our photographs were taken which explains why some of the subjects are very nicely dressed, and in the earlier pictures even appear to be wearing their best hats. It was 'not done' to visit and not pick a few sprays. With the extra family members adding to the hands around the crib, by three or four o'clock the pole-pullers would call loudly, 'No more bines, no more bines', and woe betide anyone who pulled down some more as this was the signal that the kilns were full and there were more than enough hops to be dried during the night. Sunday was a short and festive day and many people's most vivid memories are of those visits to the hopyard.

The Red Cross or Meals on Wheels benefited from the voluntary pickers who often spent days in the hopyard working at the charity crib, and it was customary for the regulars to pick a bushel or two, now and again, as their contribution.

A good picker could pick about 20-25 bushels a day when the hops were firm and the weather fine, but a good picker would also pick through bad weather and even help to clear hops when the wirework had come down and the farmer had a difficult harvest.

These vivid childhood memories of Daphne Davies's are followed by more from another local picker who remembers:

'Hop picking in the 1920s when I was a child. It was a lovely holiday as we had six weeks holiday from school in September to go hop picking. We had to be up early mornings and it was cold to go out; we had to wear warm coats as we had more than a mile to walk to Mr Adams, Avenbury Court. We always went there, there were other hopyards, Mr Price, Little Froome, Cooks the Brook House, Buckles the Hyde. The mothers took a basket with a loaf of bread, lump of butter, cheese, and perhaps a cake….

Reg, Freda and Bryon Eversham, and Elaine Cross. Bryon and Elaine are picking into an umbrella, while in the background the polepuller is tidying a fallen bine.

L to R: Gladys Bedford, ? , Joyce Blything, Mrs. Blything, Maud Evans, Bill Evans, Michael Passey, Danny Hill, Emmy Wall (sitting), Iris Wall, Dolly Corbett, and Anita and Elaine Wall.

Cribbing the unmarried girls! Lena Partridge, Adam Jones and Kate Partridge – later Mrs. Sam Jones.

Molly Littlehales, Arthur Barlow, Gladys Smith and Susan Hill at the Meals on Wheels charity crib.

This happy group, including Rose Hicks and Eva Walwyn, enjoying a cup of tea on paying-out day.

It soon came lunchtime; some people used to light a nice fire and boil their kettle for a cup of tea, do some toast, perhaps hold a slice of bacon on a stick over the fire, sometimes a kipper. It used to get a bit black but they still ate it as it smelled so nice. The children loved having a fire to have a warm by.

Sometimes you sat on some wires and picked the hops in a box or an umbrella, it gave you a rest as if you kept picking in the crib and looked about your mothers used to give you a nip across your hand and tell you to get on with picking, as when you had done one house you moved to a new one to start again.

Two or three men came a few times round the crib giving out booklets on God and preached to you, if you took no notice of them they would call you a sinner, they expected you to stand and listen to them. There was a vicarage at the top of the hopyard and the parson used to come with a basket of apples or plums and give you a few; they did not taste very nice as your hands were black and tasted of hops.

As years went by the hops went up in price to 3/- a bushel and the farmer would pay for two buses to take you into the hopyard and back about 5 o'clock at night.

When all the hopyards were picked you went to the farm to be paid and have a lump of fruit cake and a drink, they was lovely days.'

As a schoolgirl in the '30s Edith Silcock picked in the Teme Valley:

'The pickers came from the Black Country, mostly from the Lye and Dudley areas. They lived in the "barracks" and were a rough, tough crowd. Their language was colourful, to say the least. The favourite word being bloody but one rarely heard any "four lettered" words. Several members of the Salvation Army lived with them in the barracks looking after their social welfare and carrying out any necessary first aid. At the weekends buses arrived laden with their friends and relations from the Black Country and at this time things were liable to disappear – fruit from the trees, chickens from their runs and even washing from the line! They always brought their dogs with them, usually lurchers, and had a great time poaching rabbits.

The local (home) pickers were collected by bus from various pick-up points and taken to the hopyard. One of the first things to do on arriving at the crib was to make a fire with any available bits of wood, particularly on cold mornings when there was sometimes ice on the hops. After picking for an hour or so it was time for breakfast....

The bushellers usually came round three times a day. We had two in our yard, Mr D. and Mr. J. Mr D. was the local publican. He was large and jolly, and wore an old khaki shirt, baggy tweed trousers held up by large braces and nearly splitting apart over his ample middle, and an old battered trilby hat. He

Mintridge, Stoke Lacy, with the hop kiln next to the house.

Charlie Hodges bushelling at Mintridge in the 1920s.

only laughed when the women complained that he bushelled too heavily and he could hold his own when it came to bawdy comments or blue stories. Mr J. was quite the opposite being thin and wiry. He wore a cap which he turned back to front so that the peak did not get in the way as he lifted the bushel full of hops to tip into the sack the men were holding ready to receive them. He rarely smiled and did not indulge in any back-chat with the pickers. If they got too cheeky he would, accidentally of course, catch them on the head with the bushel as he bent over to take the hops out of the crib. This would lead to a stream of bad language and unfavourable comments on his parentage but he took no notice and just continued on his way.

During the afternoon various vans would visit the hopyard looking for customers, the butcher, the baker, ice cream van, etc, and the Salvation Army lassies brought along a large urn of tea on a barrow. This had a distinctive taste to it and the general opinion was that it tasted of iodine, this being due, it was said, to the urn being used to boil up the bandages used in the first aid activities. However, there were always plenty of customers when the cry of "tea-oh" was heard along the headland.

After the late afternoon bushelling everyone went home to clean up and get a cooked meal. Cleaning one's hands, which were coated with a thick film of pollen from the hops, was a problem and everyone had their favourite solution varying from washing them in paraffin to smearing them liberally with butter.'

Mollie Walwyn's first memories of hop picking were:

'Watching the Black Country pickers arriving at Bromyard Station by special train and of the farm drays awaiting them. Their tin trunks were loaded with them and taken to several farms for about three weeks picking.

When I was a little older my family went "hopping" to the Brook House, Avenbury, owned by Alfred and John Cook. We had to walk there and back and usually started out in the dark about 6 a.m. My sister, much younger than I, had a wooden truck made from an old pram to ride in.

My father who was a postman saved his holidays to come with us. The money earned usually bought us new shoes etc for the winter. Old clothes were kept during the year to wear in the fields and we waited for the "umbrella man" to come to Bromyard some weeks previously. He would exchange broken "brollies" for mended ones and the large man's umbrella was so useful in helping to keep us dry when it rained.

Some pickers took a short cut over the fields by the "Haunted Church" but it was too creepy early in the morning so round the road we went. "Strangers", as we called them lived in the buildings. One I remember very well. He was called "Darkie" and came every year with his wife to the Brook House. He would help us get a dry faggot of wood to light our fire. We boiled our kettle on an iron rack over the fire and toasted bread and rashers of bacon on a stick, catching the fat on the bread. It tasted grand. Milk could be had from the farm. Mr Alf Cook did the measuring by bushel basket himself.

Years later I used to go with a mobile shop from Burtons Stores to Instone Court to supply the pickers who lived in the farm buildings during the picking. Tom Corbett drove the van and we went there three days a week. Later still I went hopping again with my baby son. It was wartime and the Battle of Britain was raging. Every time we heard a plane we mothers grabbed the babies and tried to hide under the hop bines. Mr Robinson, a schoolmaster, used to give us each day the number of enemy planes that had been brought down during the previous day to cheers from all of us. We sometimes went to other farms to help out if we finished ours first.

Hopping to us was a real holiday, especially if the weather was good, but rain or shine we all looked forward to it.'

Molly Walwyn picking at Little Froome in the 1950s. Bill Evans, Mollie, Eva Walwyn behind Maud Evans, and Violet Lock.

In 1940 Ethel Waldron of Burley Gate Post Office drove a van shop, a converted ambulance, for the hop pickers. She used to call at Hillhampton at dinner time, and farms in Much Cowarne and Moreton Jeffries in the evenings, returning to the shop at about 10.30 pm. Here she is at Leighton Court, Much Cowarne.

Following Mollie Walwyn's memories of travelling with the mobile shop, Layton Edwards recalls how Glen Warburton and he used to take a 30-cwt van to stock up the local shops such as the Major's Arms on Fromes Hill, the Fir Tree, the Five Bridges, Hope's Rough by Bromtrees Hall and the Post Offices at Bishops Frome and Burley Gate:

'The local traders also took vans out to the hopyards and especially to supply the farm "shops" such as those at Nevilles the Dovehills and Yates the Venn. The orders were much sought after, but most farmers went to their regular grocers. The vans took bulk orders, say ½ cwt of sugar in ½ lb and 1 lb packets. Tea at 5d a quarter, a whole cheese to be cut up with knives or the shopkeeper loaned them a cheesewire. Sliced bacon was in 5 lb packs to be sold to the pickers by the slice. Woodbines were 250 for 7/- when 5 in a packet, 200 for 5/- when 10 in a packet. Twist was 8d an ounce and Best Shag 8½ d an ounce.

Saturday afternoon was time off in the hopyards. Many families stayed on the farms to do their washing, cook a special meal and rest, or they could attend the mission meetings, often organised by the Salvation Army. Others collected their "subs" and went to town. Bromyard was like a beehive, you couldn't move for people in the streets and all the pub yards were full of carts and drays. The women shopped and the men went on the scrumpy. Only the local people were allowed in the bars, so the pickers bought their drinks at the jug and bottle and drank in the pub yards.

The local policemen supplemented by the specials were constantly on patrol. Rumours of fights and knifings abounded and even the women would fight with much swearing and hair pulling, often "egged on" by their menfolk. Too much rough cider was blamed for such behaviour.'

Hop pickers outside Five Bridges Public House, the local policeman 'keeping an eye' on proceedings.

Hop-pickers' quarters in 20th century, from farm sale particulars.

(Hop acreage not always stated)

1918 Pixley, Poolend Farm, 206 acres.
In Field No. 81 there is a Shed fitted with Hop and Fruit Pickers' cubicles.

1919 Tarrington, Little Tarrington, 204 acres.
Hop-Pickers' House built of Brick and iron with Waggon and Implement Shed under.

1919 Yarkhill, Showle Court, 213 acres, 8 acres hops.
In Field No 272, are:- Extensive Brick and Iron House for Hop Pickers, and a Brick, Timber and Tile Cooking and Eating House.

1941 Tarrington, Aldersend, 420 acres, 20 acres hops.
Brick and Timber with galvanised iron roof Wainhouse with Hop-pickers' Barracks, fitted with cubicles over. The Wainhouse is fitted with grates for use as Hop-pickers' Cookhouse, 2 galvanised iron elephant huts, one fitted with sleeping apartments…. open Cattle Shed with loose box which can be used as Hop-pickers' Cookhouse.

HOP PICKERS' BARRACKS. (OLD)
MUCH COWARNE. Herefs.

CHAPTER 4

Clear 'Em Up!

In the researches for this book, letters were written to some of the Birmingham and Black Country newspapers asking people to write their memories of hop picking before the days of the machine. We were surprised to get such a large response to our enquiries and find what happy memories the old hop-picking days evoked. Of course, these letters are from older people who came hop picking as children and perhaps remember the old days with childhood affection; to their mothers hops meant hard work in good weather and bad, and a few shillings towards the family needs.

We have had to pick extracts from these letters but have tried to keep their flavour, so evocative of a past era. The editor of *The Birmingham Post & Mail*, Keith Whetstone, was the first to reply with his experiences at Nashend Farm during the Second World War:

'Although I have no experience of Bromyard, I do have lasting memories of two summers spent on a farm at Bosbury between Ledbury and Hereford, when I was 10 and 11. Apart from us kids and a few family friends, the hop pickers

Keith Whetstone and his brother with the Women's Land Army girls at Nashend Farm, Bosbury, about 1941. It is unusual to see WLA girls wearing their hats, and one suspects that the photograph was taken on a special occasion.

were Land Army girls, brought in to replace the gypsies who had traditionally provided the labour before the war. I remember Farmer Davies moaning that he never had to make any provision for the gypsies, but he had been forced to provide a proper hut and other facilities as living quarters for the girls.

I have other memories of those days – the desperate scrounging of fuel to keep the donkey engine going in the oast house; visits from my parents and friends at week-ends when we all tested our gas masks in the sulphur-laden fumes of the drying furnace room....

My, you have brought back memories. I've just recalled how we used to dig our arms into the crib and raise the hops in an attempt to lighten them just before the measuring bushel came round in the hope that they'd go further. I think we were paid 4d a bushel, but memory may have misled me.'

Once the Society's letter appeared in the press, replies came in thick and fast. The next one takes us back to the 1920s:

'I do have a few memories of the hop picking days. Sorry I have no printed facts nor photographs of those days, just memories which may help you to pursue the history and character of the farms.

As most hop pickers came from the Black Country it meant each farmer had an agent who recruited labour, namely pickers and men to cut the wires

Farmer Pudge with Black Country hop pickers at Cradley, 1920s.

(bines) and work in the kilns. These agents were women, who were also pickers, they organised the whole picking season from beginning to end, no mean
thing you will see.

Having recruited the required number of good pickers, she had to see that all
boxes and pickers were at the railway station waiting for the train, she would
see all the belongings were loaded on the train. The excitement and noise were
always almost indescribable. Many of those women and children had hardly
moved out of their Road or Street since the last hop picking season – it was
indeed a working holiday. The road leading to the railway station would be
a sight worth seeing, almost every contraption on wheels was used to convey
the boxes to the station, such as wheelbarrows, tramways, dobbins, high prams,
horse and gigs, horse and traps. The clatter of hob nailed or iron tipped shoes
added to the noise. Many a man had a day off from work to see their wives
and children on their way. In those days the journey to Hereford was a long
one, so we were very happy to arrive: Captain Edwards (who farmed at Lower
Town, Preston Wynne) would have two or three hay carts waiting at the station
to take us to the farm; first the boxes would be placed in the carts, then we
would sit on them to enjoy another slow ride along narrow lanes, off-time we
would have to duck under the overhanging trees, mostly fruit trees, the high
hedgerows were covered with blackberries and hazel nuts.

The last lap of the journey – leaving Stoke Edith station for the farm around 1908.

Mr. Jim Soley and Mr. Powell bushelling hops at Poplands about 1950. The
strings were for tying the greensacks.

On arrival at the farm boxes would be taken into the barn, most women
were very strong. Clean straw would be placed on the floor, a sheet or blanket
was placed over the straw, pillows placed in position and then other clothes.
Next item was to meet the Captain to discuss how many bushels to the shilling.
Some women inspected the hops then decided whether to accept the offer or
not, the Captain gave a speech of welcome, asked us not to take apples from
the trees on account of damage to the tree. He gave us the promise he would
sell at the end of the picking season as many apples as we wanted, at a very
cheap price; he was always true to his word. He also said if we boys helped to
pick up potatoes on a Saturday afternoon every person would have a Saturday
dinner. We boys and girls went to a little church there never seemed a welcome or any encouragement. The Salvation Army came every week and gave
everyone a real happy hour, the singing and preaching in the farmyard broke
the silence of the countryside. The first week or so many pickers could not
sleep, the silence was too much.

Now for the cribs, there were three kinds, the small, the large with a partition and the large without the partition. Sometimes Captain Edwards busheled
the hops, he was a very light busheler. His son a very heavy one and suffered
the curses of the women, and they could swear. Neither father or son would

bushel dirty hops – that is a crib of hops containing leaves. Pickers' hands would become yellow with stain, food touched by those hands would be bitter. Mornings would be very cold, afternoons very hot.'

Another letter from Birmingham:

'My parents took me hop picking before I was old enough for school. My family, relations, friends, neighbours. We went from Snow Hill Station Birmingham from the first week in September, Sunday or Monday morning about eight o'clock. I was only a small child but people waiting on the platform or getting off the trains would look at us as tho' we had come from out of space. It used to have Hop Pickers Only on the train windows and we would be shunted off and left for some time while the other trains went through. We used to go for two or three or more weeks till the hop picking was finished. To Mr Twinberrow's, White House Farm, Suckley near Worcester and Bromyard till the time I got married, nothing could keep us away. It was our working holiday. We looked forward to it from the time we came home we were waiting to get back next year. We had lots of friends, whoever got there first would have the fires lit outside our barns which we lived in…. Twinberrow had two sons, Kim and Jack. They done the busheling about three times a day. Then every other night when it was time to knock off one of them would come round to our cribs to give us a sub. We would go to the shops, my mum would cook us a dinner on the fire outside our barn. My dad and his mates would go to have a drink at the pub, The Crosskeys, just past our shop on the hill, if you walked straight on you would come to Bromyard. We used to go there to the

Wagonloads of hop pickers leaving Bromyard station for the hop farms.

Pickers from Birmingham in the hopyards at Whitbourne in the 1920s.

shops of a Saturday afternoon. People came from other parts of Birmingham and from the Black Country, West Bromwich, Cradley Heath, Dudley, Walsall. Some people came every year.

Men came down the field selling hot doughnuts, lardy cakes, ice cream, sweets and shout "Cry Baby. Cry, if your mother won't buy you some sweets. Hot faggots and peas." My mum used to take the basins and spoons down the field and bread. We all worked hard so we had good food and enjoyed it singing while we picked the hops, "Here comes the busheler to bushel up your hops" and "We are the New York dandies." Everyone joined in, never a dull moment. We used to have a barn dance up at the Crosskeys Pub Saturday night....'

A letter from Dudley emphasises the need to earn money in the hard times before the War:

'The first time I ever went hop picking I was ten years old. 1939 War was just breaking out, but that didn't really bother me, I didn't realise how awful the War would be, I was so excited to be going hopping as my mother called it. She was a widow with a family to bring up and was desperately hard up so our next door neighbour suggested hop picking. Mother was rather reluctant, she thought only common people went, but anyway poverty won and we were on our way in an old bone shaker of a coach, but us kids thought it was great, we had never been on holiday in our lives and to us we were having a month's holiday. It seemed to take hours to get to the farm (The Farm, Moreton Jeffries), it was owned by Mr Harry and Jack Baskerville not far from Bromyard, a place called Stoke Lacy. I was rather surprised to see we were to be living in a barn and sleeping on a straw bed, but it was only the thought of earwigs that bothered me. We settled down very well, there were big iron grates and we had the most beautiful coke fires, we could use as much coke as we liked. We didn't much care for getting up at the crack of dawn, but the smell of bacon and eggs cooking gave us a healthy appetite. After breakfast we would wash up and mother would cut a pile of sandwiches to take to the hop fields complete with kettle of water, tea, sugar and milk. By the time I had carried the kettle of water and picked a few apples there was usually only half a kettle of water left.

Although we were only children we were expected to work all day long, except for dinner hour – ours was usually two hours because my brother and I used to have to fetch firewood to light the fire in the hopyard on which to boil the kettle, but once we could get away from work we used to go into the orchard for apples – I remember eating 10 apples one day with no effect on my stomach.

Mr Baskerville, both Harry and Jack, were very nice, they didn't mind anyone having the apples so long as the trees were not damaged. On Sunday mornings Harry would let everyone have as many potatoes they needed and didn't charge anything for them. Also, every Sunday he would sell rabbits for about 6d and 9d each, and carrots and onions. We used to have rabbit stew, my mother was a smashing cook, they tasted really good and we would follow on with lovely apple dumpling. We were extremely healthy kids, and we were always kept very clean and tidy.

We used to wait for the ice cream van to come to the hop fields so that we could have a 1d wafer, and about two fields away there was a little pub called the Three Crowns. We used to fetch fresh crusty bread from there, also Smith's crisps at 1d per packet. Some of the neighbours used to come into the fields to pick hops. One dear old lady used to bring tomatoes from her greenhouse to sell 4d per pound. The Septembers then were beautiful, it hardly ever rained, we used to be as brown as berries. We even used to pray for rain so that we could play instead of picking hops, although most of the time we really worked hard for our mother because we knew the money would be for our new winter clothes for school.

About three nights each week it would be Sub Night, that meant you could sub some of the money you had earned to keep yourselves. Every Sub Night I would go and hide because I didn't want to be seen fetching money. I used

Mrs. Morgan frying on a brazier or 'devil', under cover but not in the barn for fear of fire in the buildings.

A hop picker kitchen (army style). Bell tent accommodation in background.   *Brian Willder*

to think it was very degrading but my mother only used to have 10/- widow's pension plus 5/- for my brother and 3/- each for my sister and myself, and used to have to pay 11/3 rent out of that, no wonder she used to have to take washing and sewing in to make ends meet. No rent rebate or family allowance in those days.

After that first year my mother went every year. I used to pack my job up to go till I was 18 years old. I'd soon get another job within a few days of getting home.

It used to be lovely at night, we would sit around the fires singing all the old songs and about 9.30 p.m. Harry would come and pour water on all the fires because of air raids, and we used to go to bed.

It was amazing really, so many people living rough and yet everyone got on so well, never any rows or trouble, and the men had their own sleeping quarters. Not even married couples could sleep together. The women's room was quite a distance from the men's. When we were coming home the farmer would sell best apples very cheap, also Victoria plums 1d per pound. I had to fetch 24 lbs once for making jam at the grand total of 2/-. Although I have enough money now to go on holiday anywhere in the world, I could never ever be so happy as I was down on Baskerville's farm.'

In similar vein and expressing very vividly the urgent excitement of childhood comes this letter from Tipton:

'…My mother, brother, grandma and I went hop picking every year for over 25 years and to the same farm. It was just outside the Bromyard area (Hill Farm, Stanley Hill, Bosbury). Miss Cotton and her niece, Nan Clews, ran the farm. Two wonderful and kindly ladies. I remember Miss Cotton as a very old lady who wore a long black dress with a white apron over it. In her pocket she always carried mints and used to give us poor kids a few nearly every day. Miss Nan (as we called her) was such a kindly person also. She always had a smile and a kind word for us. She inherited the farm when Miss Mary Ann Cotton passed away. The farm was rather small with just two hopyards. Therefore about 25 people used to go for the hop picking. The same families turned up every year. In fact, it was like meeting one's own family once a year. There was also Mr and Mrs Dixon, they were gypsies, they also came every year with their family and parked their caravan in a field behind the kilns.

From June the only thing in our minds was how long before we were to go on our annual holiday to the hopyards. We counted the days, getting prepared a few days before the final day arrived was so exciting. Mother would check the old tin hop picking box to see what bit of tin food she had collected to take with us. There never was a great deal as my dad was on the means test and the money we had to live on wasn't much. We relied on neighbours and relatives to give us a bit of sugar or a quarter of tea and such like to take with us. At last the great day arrived, the night before we would have had a bath in the old tin tub before the fire, mother would take a last look in our hair to see that we had no nits and so to bed, not to sleep, we were much too excited to sleep, thinking of the great day ahead. Up at six (the train was about 10 a.m. we didn't want to be late). Dad would borrow the neighbour's trolley to take the hop picking box to the station. At last there we were on the platform waiting with all our friends from last year for the train. Here it comes. Oh the excitement, mother makes sure the box is put in a safe place in the guard's van. Into the carriage we all get and off we go. On the journey we kids would be planning what we were going to do when we got to paradise (that was what the dear old farm was to us).

When we were well on our way, out of her basket mother would get the loaf and a jam jar, the jar was filled with margarine, she would then proceed to cut two hunks of bread and marge. We would relish it. She would say, "That will last you until we get there."

Then arriving at Ledbury station out of the station we kids would rush to see if the farmhands, Mike Palmer and Mr Jenkins was there with the two great shire horses and farm cart. Sure enough, there they would be on the forecourt. Back to the station we would run to help to carry the boxes for them to be loaded onto the cart. Sitting on the boxes and away we would go to travel five miles this way.'

Collecting greensacks at Merryfield, Stoke Lacy. Esne Jones at the horse's head.

Here is a memory from a man living in Rowley Regis who went hop picking before the First World War:

'Hop picking was a delight to us children, we looked forward to it more than Xmas. Oddly enough my first hop picking trip is my best remembered. It was before the First World War. I think 1912… I think why I remember so long ago is because an incident happened one day. My mother had got my youngest brother to sleep and lay him in the hop vines, out of the sun. Presently the big cart horse that collected the bags of hops stopped dead and would not move, everybody was saying what's wrong with the horse he's never been like that before, then my mother shouted with horror, "My child is nearly under the cart wheel." The horse knew that and was fed with apples for days after.

About ½ mile up the road was a little shop and a kindly woman served me with some things. After that she took my dry bread sandwich off me and put a slice of meat in between, and several times after. People were very good then. Every evening after work, the master would dish out jugs of cider and firewood for our fires at night. Any eggs the fowls had laid away under the hedgerows we could keep. That and collecting apples to take back home was my job…. I remember the big walnut tree at the bottom of the drive. We used to throw up at them to knock them off for Xmas and get our hands covered in walnut stains. Then the master would say, "See you have been at my nuts again." He had a lot of guinea fowl, they would fly on to the barns and make a cry like, "Come back! Come back!" People would shout, "We will! We will!".'

Another nonagenarian looks back:

'As I shall be 90 years of age this November 18th (1984) your letter to the Birmingham Post Tuesday November 13th (1984) brought back to me vivid memories of living in Bromyard as a young child. I think I was only 7 or 8 when we left Bromyard for Birmingham. As a child I suffered from anaemia badly and my mother was told that I should be taken to the hop fields from sunrise to sunset for the good of my health, and when the school holidays started off we went, Mother, a brother two years older and another brother 2½ years younger. If the hop picking season was not finished when the school holiday was over that school holiday was extended much to our delight. Given fine weather it was a delightful time for all of us….

We children took old umbrellas which were opened and the ends stuck into the ground, and we picked into those earning a few coppers occasionally when we were not foraging around the fields for apples.

I think my memory is right in saying that the price then for picking was 8 pennies a bushel, a straight up wicket basket – it did take a long time to pick a bushel.

The women pickers chatted and seemed a happy crowd. The farmer brought round churns of hot milk about mid morning and when we had a break to eat I can remember the joy of eating herrings and bloaters toasted over a sort of camp fire.

At sunset we packed up and walked home quite a long way, very grubby and very tired.

When all the hop picking was over an old custom took place. All the farm men who had cut down the bines, measured the bushels or picked hops and carted them away, had their fun. They cribbed all the old ladies, which meant they upended them into the cribs – a sight not to be forgotten.

A very dim memory, I can remember standing in the Square end of the main street for celebrating the Relief of Mafeking.

Also my two brothers and myself had Scarlet Fever and we were taken to the fever hospital at the foot of the Downs where we were fed on milk puddings for weeks and weeks and chickens wandered in and out of the ward, all still a vivid memory.'

This yard in Acton Beauchamp may have been strung using the Butcher system of wirework invented in Kent in 1875, in which there were three horizontal wires: at ground level, waist high and at the top of the poles. Coir strings for each stock were taken to the middle wire and then sloped to the top wire of the adjacent row. The kettle hangs over the fire ready to replenish the teapot. However, Nurse Powell has brought her own thermos.

A letter full of incident and wealth of detail came from West Bromwich:

'I was interested in your letter in the *Express* and *Star* and I hope this may be of some help to your worthy effort to portray the life in the hop-fields around Bromyard. I am 58 years old and went hop picking when I was born and many times from then on. I was left in my pushchair in the middle of a field at Tenbury when my mother was chased by a very angry bull. I was then 18 months old and needless to say, I survived that not very nice ordeal. At that time parties of pickers went from all over the Black Country, about 40-strong. They were organized by a leader who had been appointed by the hop grower, usually someone who had gone for donkeys' years as they used to say…. Some travelled by train to Stourbridge junction and on to Stourport. There they were met by farm carts and taken to their farms. People from different areas went to their particular farms and were known as the Tipton lot, Cradley and Old Hill lot, Smethwick lot, Bromsgrove lot and so on. They mostly consisted of women and older men. Only a few younger men went and a good few of these were men who strangely enough would not work at home although there were jobs. They were called Rodneys in the Black Country slang. That is not to say they were all idlers as there were no easy jobs in the hopyards…. Children, as in my case, were not allowed to leave until they had picked a quota set by their mothers. The best part of the day was when tea was brewed and sandwiches handed out; bread and jam was the normal thing and wasps created a nuisance – I've had many a painful sting. The stains on the fingers tasted very bitter from the hops but it was not often we could wash our hands, nevertheless we enjoyed our food. One of the worst aspects of the picking was rainy weather but it was no excuse to stop work unless of course it was too extreme. The red sticky mud was awful sometimes inches deep and towards the end of hop picking it was not unknown to find ice on the hops. Usually people picked five and a half days with the weekend optional; some picked on the weekends and the hops had to stay in the cribs until Monday. Needless to say, some were stolen and put in other cribs by rogues; mostly though so poor, most pickers were honest enough. True there were some riff-raffs who came from all over the country and they gave pickers a bad name. There were some characters and likeable rogues. There were travellers who came year after year and their caravans were so spotless you could eat off the floor. They were not to be confused with tinkers and the like. I made several good lasting friendships with many of the travellers.

Living quarters were rough and sometimes everyone slept in the same barn, divided off by blankets strung over strings. Some were separate stalls with whitewashed walls and clean straw was put on the floors for bedding. The beds were made up in the morning by turning the straw over with a stick. There was not too much privacy in these places and it was embarrassing when the visitors came at weekends, usually the husbands; the sounds of passion were heard very often but in those days the significance escaped me. When we

Hop pickers' quarters at Suckley. This hut was considered a superior type for conscientious pickers only. The kitchen on the left was only partly enclosed. Mr. and Mrs. Griffiths with their grandchildren, about 1960.

arrived once during the War (1940) the first in got the best places. The farmer who had his place near the Seven Stars and Red Lion at Cradley, handed out a supply of blankets to everyone of us. He was classed as a good gaffer. He also gave out a ration of potatoes every day. That year the army were called in to do some picking alongside us which was well appreciated by the teenaged girls (and some cheating women). It was not unusual to see them sneak off among the bushes. The troops had to return to unit every night so they made hay while the sun shone.

There was also a tribe of true Romanies who spoke their own language and had a convoy of horse-drawn caravans – this was a sight to see.

The mornings began when a large fire was made outside the quarters. This was done by a man paid by the pickers themselves; he collected the wood, if it was not supplied by the farmer, chopped it up and put all the smoke-blackened pots, pans and kettles on to boil. This was for washing and making tea. Then there was the delicious smell of bacon cooking to go with the fried eggs; fresh milk was available but I well remember the condensed and evaporated milk. Sandwiches were taken to the hopyards and we had a cooked meal on coming back in the evening, mainly stew made from tinned steak and vegetables bought from the locals very cheaply. The farmer came every night to hand out subs (advances of earnings) to those who wanted money but there was always some to take home at the end of the season.

The pubs in the locality did a roaring trade from the hundreds of pickers. The scrumpy cider was cheap and plentiful and the pubs were lively places to say the least! I have seen many a fight and the main culprits seemed to be the travellers who were banned from some pubs or confined to the bar only. I well remember the Hereford House, the Nelson, Red Lion and Seven Stars all in the Suckley and Cradley areas. My favourite though was Polly Beards' which was a cottage with an off-licence. They sold the brew most of the Black Country people knew. We were served through an open window and drank from bottles we took out of crates; these we washed with water out of a hand pump. We could not drink on the premises so we went through a hole in the hedge to a hop field twenty yards away. If it was cold (it usually was) the licensee made a huge bonfire and we all sat round and either sang our heads off or listened to the tales told by the travellers. They were varied and always interesting stories

The Herefordshire House, Stanford Bishop. Mr. and Mrs. Jones with their daughter Lily.

Polly Beard's Off Licence at Suckley.

of country lore. One man brought a jackdaw with him and he let it fly into the trees until we went home – it talked very well. Old Eva came lunch-time and evening every day to drink her cider. She was a mysterious woman and always sat alone. When she died, the locals collected for her burial.

When the hops were finally picked and the day came to go home we said our goodbyes and packed. The trunks were heavy with apples and pears as well as a sprig of hops.

Strangely enough home seemed a luxury what with hot water and baths and home comforts. I still visit there to this day and still see old friends from way back. I also see the ghosts of former characters in my mind's eye....'

It is difficult to follow a letter which brings such a marvellous vibrant picture of hop-picking days but let us look at the other side of the coin and a letter from South Wales presents a much less rosy picture:

'Tredegar in the period 1910 to 1940 sent many families to pick hops. As the season for picking was in September having an extended holiday was looked forward to. Masters and Education Authorities accepted the longer holidays as, sad to say, most of the children hop picking were not very interested in learning. They were conscious of the fact that as children of poor families, work was their future. Grammar school was for those that could afford that kind of life. The Tredegar areas that provided hop pickers were known as the Back of the Globe, Red Lion Square, Iron Row, Iron Street. On a Sunday morning in the picking season of 1945 I and some friends travelled to Bromyard to visit the Tredegar people. Quite frankly I was astonished to see the conditions. Stables, cowsheds, barns made up the living quarters. But what jealousy existed as families claimed priority due to the number of years they had worked at this particular farm. There was always an old lady in charge of each family, men stayed at home as they worked in the pits. Hay and ferns provided the bedding. Sheets, blankets and sacking making a rather uncomfortable bed. It was really great seeing the cooking arrangement. A very large open sided brazier out in the centre of the yard, a roaring log fire and half a dozen frying pans – what a feast, sausage and mash, bacon and boiled spuds and rabbit stew. Toilet facilities were non existent, any bush away from the yard. On the whole it was looked on first as a holiday in the country, very healthy and a few pounds in the pocket.

A typical group having an evening drink in the hopyard next door to Polly Beard's.

At that time gypsies and didicoys were the serious pickers. There was plenty of fights, always during the evenings at the local pubs. Glass smashing became too expensive so landlords introduced a new drinking habit – no pint or half pint glasses, instead a quart jug and half a dozen finger glasses for each table. There is no doubt this was a working holiday only for the tough, one could not afford to be squeamish or timid. The women folk were able to look after their families and could dish out punishment if needed. People always criticised the lack of hygiene at the hop fields but the children always looked so healthy on returning home. The sulphur fumes from the kilns being a good cure for many ailments….'

The gang leader who collected people to go hop picking was the very important link between the farmers in the hop picking areas and the hop pickers in the Black Country. Mrs Ann Wright from Dudley was such a gang leader, and her son, Lawson, has provided a good picture:

'She used to pick at Ankerdine Farm, Knightwick before coming to Mr Ted Holloway's farm at The Lower House, Stanford Bishop. Her mother, Mrs Smith, was picking hops in this district as early as 1880-1890. Mrs Smith used to travel from Dudley with a cart drawn by two donkeys. Many hop pickers had their own transport of this sort and their animal stayed with them for the four or five weeks of hop picking. Many families were self employed and those with horses and carts often dealt in scrap iron, rags, etc. The Guest family had

Hop Devil.

two horses and a covered wagon in which they slept; they were general dealers and regarded as well off. Other families worked in other Black Country trades such as drain making and iron and steel moulding.

During the War Mrs Ann Wright was in war work rope making, but she still brought a gang to Stanford Bishop for their holidays. She used to meet Mr Holloway in the White Horse Inn, Bromyard, in advance and then organised her gang of pickers, probably a dozen or more who were her neighbours or work mates. A gang leader was very particular about the members of the gang as they wanted the work to go well and smoothly. The same people with their families tended to come year after year. Every worker had 12d when they were hired paid by the farmer. When hop picking started the workers were paid by the bushel. Before 1939 the rate was 12d for two bushels; it then improved to 10d a bushel and steadily increased thereafter. A good picker, probably helped by children, could manage 25 bushels a day, but the average was 16 bushels…. On occasions the hop pickers did strike for more pay and this was negotiated by the gang leader who looked after the welfare of the gang. At the Lower House there could well have been 50 pickers from Dudley with perhaps 20 children. In addition there were probably another six local pickers. There were seven acres of hops on this particular farm and the labour needed during picking was about ten pickers to the acre.'

In a letter from Kingstanding we have more details of the social life of the hop pickers and of the gang leader, in this case a man:

'From the time I was born I was taken hop picking on the Hop Pickers special train from Snow Hill Station, Birmingham, every year up to the time my father died in 1939 … we had to get up at 5.00 a.m. in the early hours to have a quick breakfast and then help my dad with the old tin trunk onto his tatting cart and push it from Aston to Snow Hill station where we got a trolley loaded with luggage, took it down the lift to the platform and took it to the train at the side platform; all the pickers were there with shouting and crying kids pushing onto the train. We had no corridors so we had to use a bucket in the carriage for a toilet and it was thrown out of the window while the train was moving. Our destination was Suckley, near Worcester, not far from Bromyard … the hops were picked into cribs made of crossed poles with sacking. The hops were bushelled out of the cribs at a shilling a bushel in a bushel basket by the foreman … the hops were bagged into large sacks and carted to the kiln or oast house to dry. Our hands became black to the knuckles because of the sulphur sprayed on the hops and we had to use paraffin to clean it off. When we pulled the last wire we cheered and cribbed the young girls and covered them with dead bines. They were the best days of my life and I've loved the country ever since. I miss the "crib up" cry when a house was finished.

My father, Charles Gordon, was hired by the farmer Mr J. Field of Pewcroft

Farm, Suckley to hire fifty pickers and their families for employment in September. He then received railway tickets by post to bring them to Suckley. My father then received one shilling per head as a bonus.

On the first day of picking my father went round the hop field to look at the size of the hops, if they were small he bargained for more money per bushel, if they were large the farmer bargained for less per bushel; in all the years we only had one strike for more money. There were two kinds of cribs, one family size and the other single size. We cut the bines on the bottom and pulled it down. Some hops were scattered on the floor and they had to be picked up before you moved your crib to another house or section to pick. Hop picking was a working holiday for the poor families of the cities, it was a healthy and profitable pastime in those days but there was a snag – my father was summoned and fined ten shillings for keeping us away from school for a month, but we, the children, enjoyed it…'

A letter came from a farm worker's son which emphasises the year round importance of the hop cultivation:

'…Before the War my young life was spent among the hop fields of Hereford and Worcester. My earliest memories date back from 1926 until 1938 when I went into the forces but came back to Redditch to live after the War in 1946.

My father, a farm worker, had a comprehensive knowledge of hops and worked at all the various stages and, as such, so were the whole family. My earliest memories around 1926 were when hops were grown up poles, not strings…. The season for us was not just the picking, it all started after the last hop was picked, the clearing and burning of the bines, the cuttings taken for new stock, the ploughing and fertilizing, the tying, the leafing, the spraying, so many vivid memories. Watching the growth until the appearance of the burrs to try to judge the quality of the crop. One thing which fascinated me a lot was the stringing in which my father was very proficient. I don't know how it is done these days but years ago it was by the use of a simple gadget on the end of a long pole which we called a monkey, and when it was finished looking across the hop field revealed a large diamond pattern. My earliest memories were of the square type rigid crib and the folding crib coming in about the mid Thirties. Where only one person or a couple were picking the crib was divided by a canvas partition for two families. Memories of the men called pole pullers, non-existent toilet facilities, the vendors who visited the hop fields, the ice cream man with his motor cycle box sidecar attachment containing soft ice cream, the well known lady from Ledbury, Hannah Brace, with her basket of kippers, bloaters etc (who, incidentally, only died around the mid Seventies). Memories of the cold and frosty mornings, the fires built for the pickers to warm up their cans and kettles and make their crude barbecues of sausages, bacon and fish etc, bushelling time comments, the camp fires at night.   The accommodation for the pickers provided by the farmers was in sheds, barns, stables and even pig-styes which had previously been thoroughly cleaned, whitewashed and clean straw provided for bedding....'

Let us finish with an extract from a letter from Wordsley, near Stourbridge. The writer used to stay with 'Farmer Pudge, Frogend Farm, Bishops Frome, near Bromyard', and she writes:

'...How funny our lives come in a circle because looking over the years as a child, I looked upon hop picking as a happy holiday time; in my teens and twenties I went through a stage of being ashamed to let my trendy friends know I even knew what hop picking was, and now in my forties I am here telling you about it with happy memories and pride at being part of a little bit of history...'

The Priest family at Frogend Farm, September 1950.

CHAPTER 5

Hymns, Health and Holidays

'Owing to the lengthy hop-picking it is found impossible to reopen the School (Whitbourne) until Monday October 7th. It is hoped that the parents will under no circumstances keep their children from School after that date.'

Bromyard Deanery Magazine, September 1901.

The many thousands of hop pickers who came into the countryside required a great deal of care and organisation, involving the local Churches, medical services, police and education authorities. But first the pickers had to be brought to the district and this was the responsibility of the railways and later, road transport. The *Bromyard News and Record* of 31 August 1905 has details of the arrival at Bromyard that week of the hop pickers' special trains, and lists the number of pickers, not counting the numerous children, destined for various farms in the district:

'Numbers on Monday, August 28
90	Mr W. Leake	(Ullingswick)
70	Mr J. Leake	(Morton Jeffries)
100	Mr E. Pudge	(Bishops Froome)
90	Mr Pudge	(Bishops Froome)
10	Mr J. Bayliss	(Ullingswick)
12	Mr J. Thomas	(Ullingswick)
20	Mr J. Davies	(Leominster)

Tuesday August 29
50	Mr Green	(Bishops Froome)
14	Mr J. Hodges	(Stoke Lacy)
50	Mr Perry	(Much Cowarne)
25	Mr Pannier	(Much Cowarne)
40	Mr Ware	(Ullingswick)
60	Mr Parker	(Little Froome)
60	Mr W. Smith	(Mayfields)
50	Mr Dupper	(Stoke Lacy)

Wednesday August 30
40	Mr Birchley	(The Heath)
40	Mr Denney	(Hopton)
60	Mr G. A. Treasure	(Felton)
60	Mr Buckle	(The Hyde)
40	Mr Adney	(Much Cowarne)
16	Mr H. Taylor	(Avenbury)'

In addition, 1,000 hop pickers had been dropped at Knightwick and 400 at Suckley on the Wednesday, while two more specials were expected the following Sunday.

By the '30s, motorcoaches were also being used for transporting pickers. Two of Gilbert Bowler's lorries from Bishops Frome would fetch pickers from South Wales in the morning and from the Black Country in the afternoon. During the war this was encouraged by the licensing authorities to relieve the pressure on the trains and buses. Two coaches and a lorry were needed to bring the pickers from the Cannock, Hednesford and Dudley area to the Parkers at Instone Court, Bishops Frome, and when they went home there would be a second luggage lorry paid for by the pickers and loaded with apples and other fruit.

The local churches were most concerned about the welfare of the pickers, while at the same time taking the opportunity for a little evangelising. The *Bromyard Deanery Magazine* reported that five children had been baptised at Thornbury on 22 September 1901. The next year, at Much Cowarne and Moreton Jeffries, the vicar ran a hop pickers' mission with the help of Mr Collier, a cadet in the Church Army, at the end of which there were eight baptisms. Mr Collier who 'was most zealous in his work among the Pickers', had stayed with Colonel and Mrs Bourne at Cowarne Court. An entry for Stanford Bishop in 1905 reads:

'The Hop Pickers Mission last year was very encouraging, our visitors so appreciating what was then done for them, that probably most of the growers will be glad to join in doing something of the sort during the coming season. Even if we are not able to support a regular Missioner this year, it is very possible that we might have a series of lantern services, lectures upon domestic and sanitary subjects, etc.

HOP PICKERS' BARRACK.
MUCH COWARE · HEREFS.

Addresses upon these matters will pass without attention in TOWN, but here in the country the pickers will welcome any evening recreation.

Most of the people are very fond of singing and it is proposed to arrange some musical evenings for them. We are sure that the young people who helped in this way last year will do so again. And the occasional tea or coffee is a great comfort after a day in the fields. The cost is not much, and if each grower and farmer would only contribute their "mite" towards the necessary outlay, the little refreshment might be given nearly every evening as an attraction to the meeting.'

Four pickers had died in the area and the prose of the period describes how:

'The painfully sudden death of a hop picker on the 5th inst. cast quite a gloom over the Parish. Abednego Richards had come from Wolverhampton with a party of hop pickers to work at the Hyde....'

Once a week, two Wesleyan Methodists, Miss Rose Moore the founder of the Boys' Own Brotherhood in Bromyard and Miss Kate Lewis, travelled out to Avenbury to hold a service in the hopyard at Munderfield Court. Miss Lewis played the harmonium which was brought from the house on a wagon. The pickers' children at Munderfield Court also attended Sunday School, along with some of their mothers who took advantage of the opportunity to learn to read and write. As already mentioned, on some farms members of the Salvation Army looked after the pickers.

In the '30s, a deaconess from Bristol with as many as six young girls preparing to be missionaries in Africa, would come to Bishops Frome to administer to the sick children. As everyone gathered round to sing and listen to her preaching, the gypsies used to take her under their wing, carry the organ and see that no one removed the light or pump from her bike.

During September there were no holidays or days off for doctors or nurses, and Philip Crosskey writes:

'Epidemics used to spread easily through the hop pickers' quarters which were crowded and rather primitive; as the weather could turn cold and wet, throat and chest infections were very common. A call to visit one family might result in seeing another half dozen families on the same farm and, with such difficult conditions, many had to go into hospital who would normally have been looked after at home. The maternity services in the area were provided by a devoted band of midwives who could tell many a story of babies delivered safely on straw palliasses by the light of hurricane lamps, and it was often said that the gypsies stayed in the area in order to avail themselves of these excellent facilities. At the Bean House, Cradley, their babies always seemed to arrive at hop-picking times, and Nurse Boucher, the district nurse, made sure of her £2 fee first in each case, as they were apt to depart at once after the child was born. Dr S. W. Russell, a general practitioner in Bromyard, was a noted obstetrician and was often reported to have spent nights on the straw in the hop pickers' quarters waiting for the final stages of labour and prepared to do fine midwifery under appalling conditions.

Hop picking was also a busy time in the surgery, especially in the evenings and at weekends when the picking had finished, and the small cramped waiting room at Nunwell House would reek of the acrid smell of hops. Of course, there were all the incidental accidents that happened on farms when there was such intense activity in progress. Wasp stings were common amongst the children who used to walk around with a 'piece', the jam spread all over the face and hands.

As a newcomer to the practice, it was not easy to grasp the pressing need to get the hop driers well enough to keep on with their work. They had tremendous loyalty to the farmer and the farm, and intense interest in proving their worth as driers by producing the best samples of hops. A lapse in the care of the drying process could be disastrous, so the drier and his health were the key to a successful hop picking.

Of course there were the skivers amongst the hop pickers who were on the sick list at home and wanted to continue drawing sick pay whilst earning money hop picking. Then there was the occasional patient who fell ill towards the end of hop picking and "needed" an ambulance to get home! But these were the few; the many kept well and the children always looked fitter and browner at the end of their month in the hopyards.

BARN & HOP PICKERS ACCOM? AT LOWER COURT FARM BUCKLEY.

September is now much as any other month and the barracks and huts stand empty, mute reminders of all the noise, bustle and activity of the old hop picking days.'

The doctors were not the only ones to have their leave stopped. Constable Fred Harris was a well-known character in Bishops Frome who kept very firm control during the influx. He was a big, brawny man who made a point of knowing by name all the gypsies and many of the imported pickers, and could quickly apprehend any wrongdoers often dispensing instant justice on the spot in the shape of a heavy clout; Mrs Harris would have two extra constables billeted on her during the season. Other well-remembered names include P.C. Penry and 'Gunboat' Smith from Tarrington.

The start of the Autumn Term in hop-growing areas used to be delayed until after hop picking, but by 1952-3 a change in the dates of the school holidays to coincide with those for the rest of the country was causing a conflict of interests for parents of school children, both locally and in the Black Country: if the children were kept away from school their parents faced a fine in the magistrates' courts. The earlier start to the term, an increase in the numbers of children attending the Grammar School because of the 1944 Education Act, two cold, late hop-picking seasons and an active campaign by the Local Education Authority against children missing school for hop picking, engendered considerable debate at the time which is reflected in the following extracts from the *Bromyard News and Record*:

Lower Court, Suckley – the hop pickers' fireplaces.   *Joan Grundy*

18 September 1952 The Hop Harvest:

Hop farmers in the Bromyard district must be very well satisfied with the crops which are now being picked, and are in many cases above average.

Hop pickers had a good start to their holiday with pay but last week found the weather rather trying. It is most unusual to contend with North and East winds for a whole week and there must have been many very cold fingers especially amongst the very young.

The hop machines and the fines for children kept away from school seem to have had an effect on the number of outside pickers coming to the district. Local pickers have found employment either in picking or tending the machines.

18 December 1952 – A report of the National Farmers Union AGM:

Mr. N. D. O. Capper, branch delegate to the Hop Committee, told members that the committee was concerned that all schools were beginning the Autumn term at the same time, which was when hop picking commenced. They felt it was a very serious matter and hoped it would be possible to go back to the old system. Representatives of the Committee were to consult the Director of Education and his committee on the matter.

17 September 1953 Hop Picking and the Schools:

Many schools in the hop-area are finding the number of absentees, since the term began on Tuesday, very high indeed. At Brockhampton, for instance, over 25 per cent were absent, while at Ashperton the percentage was still higher.

On Wednesday, Bromyard Senior School had 56 absent out of a total of 231. Many parents had sent for and filled in and returned forms due to taking their annual holidays from their employment for this fortnight. In some few cases these filled-in forms may have been meant for real holidays, but the majority undoubtedly were meant in order to go hop picking and take the children along.

The first question which therefore arises is whether hop picking possibly on the same farm as that on which the father is already employed, is "from my employment". The next is, if the mother signs the form as parent, is she on annual holiday if she does not leave home except to walk to and work in the hop yards?

If the answer to these two questions, or either of them, is "yes", then it seems that the filling in of the forms is a mere farce and a waste of paper, and that the best thing to do is to return to having the annual summer holiday in hop areas in late September and October as in most schools in previous years. If the answer is "no" then the parents should realise that they are in danger of prosecution.

It would be helpful if the Education Authorities would give an answer to the questions so the parents would know just where they stand.

It quite obviously is not fair on the school teachers to have to start a new year, with children beginning in new forms, when only half to three-quarters of them are present, and in a fortnight's time they will have to begin all over again on the others when they come back.

There is also bound to be a waste of public money in buses running to the schools with only a handful of children in them, or, as in the case of Fromes Hill to Ashperton last Tuesday morning with none being picked up at Fromes Hill.

Also, presumably, even if no dinners were wasted on the first day, the full canteen staffs had to be paid for cooking dinners for far fewer children than usual.

This matter is a serious one for all concerned, and it is essential that a satisfactory solution shall be worked out immediately to ensure that the winter term in 1954 begins with all children being present at their schools.

24 September 1953 Hop Picking and the Weather:

The hop pickers in the Bromyard district have so far had little help from the weather, which has varied between a little sun, sudden storms, and wild winds.

Hop pickers returning home with their trunks and bunches of hops. Stoke Edith station around 1908.

The number of pickers has fallen considerably, due to the growing number of machines now in use, and also due to the healthy respect that sharp fines last year for keeping children away from school, engendered in the minds of many parents from the Birmingham and Dudley areas.

Where machines are used work has continued in all but the very worst weather, and another two or three weeks should see it all over.

8 October 1953 – A report of the previous week's Rural District Council meeting:

Inspection of Hop Pickers' Accommodation by Dudley Education Department.

The Clerk reported that he had written to the Education Department of the Dudley Council asking if a deputation had been visiting local farms to inspect the accommodation of hop pickers' children and stating the Council's disapproval of any such inspection without their knowledge.

This matter had been raised by the Surveyor in the Housing and Health Committee meeting, and the Medical Officer had objected strongly to such a visit.

In reply to his letter the Clerk said that they (the Dudley Council) regretted that the visit had taken place without the Council being notified. They had no intention of interfering with the Council's administration, but it has been the practice for a number of years for members of their Education Committee to visit farms and see how the children were accommodated. Apologies were made and it was stated that in future the Council should be told of proposed visits.

The end of an era was not to be delayed, and by 1960 employment at the local glove factory, in the school meals service and at the hospital had absorbed the nimble fingers and willing hands, and provided a more regular income for many married women. The children's education had become more important than the hop-picking money.

By the end of the twentieth century, the recruitment of reliable hop pickers for the complete harvest period was becoming more difficult. British people no longer wished to spend four or five weeks of their holiday picking hops, and those who had no work were reluctant to take employment for a few weeks only. Hop growers began to find that students from Europe, particularly Poland, were keen to take work on British farms and so began a regular seasonal migration.

Lara Latcham, of Herefordshire Museum's Heritage Services, realised the significance of this new generation of hop-pickers. During the 2005 hop harvest, Kim Jones from Bromyard Heritage Centre talked to Adam, Karolina, Magda and Arek during breaks from their work on an old-established hop farm, where hops had been grown since the 1880s. The farm's owner explained that six or seven overseas workers had arrived on a university student scheme in 1990, mainly from cities in northern Poland, and by 2005 the number had grown to eighteen men and women. With a little training they were capable of all jobs – those with most experience working in the kilns, others cutting bines, tractor driving, or hanging hops on the bine track. They were hard workers and those returning year after year had become much like family.

Successive enlargements of the European Union have opened up opportunities for season workers from other eastern European countries.

HOP TOKENS.

CHAPTER 6

A Farmer's Diary

'Here are four harvests, the hay; the corn; the hop and the cider.'

John Clarke, 1794.

The late Ted Holloway of Lower House, the Bull Ring and Hope House in Stanford Bishop, and Sevington in Acton Beauchamp, kept a series of day books covering the years 1951 to 1977.

Not all the events listed below occurred in any one year, but an attempt has been made to show the working year on a mixed farm, where hops were only one of many enterprises, by condensing the twenty-seven year span of entries into twelve months.

January

Plant hop roots. Trimmed hopyard hedge. Lower House hops sampled. Repaint barn in top yard. To Rosemaund to buy 84 wire work posts. 6 tons of slag spread on bottom hopyard. Hopgrowers' meeting. Bought 36 hop poles. Snow and heavy drifting during night. Ditched Landrover at Hawkins. Met Ministry man re kilns. Plough up hops. 6 tons of bones. Squaring up accounts from hop-picking.

February

Pegged out wirework. Ploughing finished except for hops. Plough down hops. Received hop valuations. Trimming inside hopyard hedge. Death of the King (1952), muck spreading. King's funeral, good weather. Muck hauling. Currant planting. Stocking hops. Winter washed currants. George had lorry to haul posts from Rosemaund, broke down on way home. Finished ploughing currants and started hops. Put artificial on hops. Fencing around bottom hopyard. Wages up to £12 8s. per week (1969).

March

New tractor. Ploughed down hops at Bull Ring, working on wirework. Started cutting hops. Put some K nitro on hops. Nitro chalk on currants. Beechams man called re currants. Throwing down and cutting hops. Wonderful weather. Sowing. Manure on currants and hops, spreader broken. Finished ploughing and cutting hops. Picked up a few cuttings. Planting hop roots. Started to spread shoddy. Poles came to all farms. Ernie wireworking. Cutting hop pegs.

April

Harrowed hops. Sprayed currants. Red Rum won Grand National. Planted currant cuttings. Spreading shoddy on hops. String arrived. Getting reversion out of currants. G. to London re hops. Stringing. Hop pegging. Planted oats in hopyard at Sevington. Muck from big shed to Bull Ring. Harrow currants. Mr D. and others here re hop-picking machine. Planted potatoes between currants.

May

Women hop tying. 3 Bromyard women bracing. Finished rotavating currants. All staff hop tying. Hop insurance man. See vicar of Bromyard re electricity in church. Cold all week, nothing growing, hops very backward. Finished hooking and stringing. Put phosphate on first hopyard. 3 Bromyard women doing hops second time. Sprayed currants.

George Holloway, Harry Brooks, Fred Anthony (stockman, busheller and dryer) and Ted Holloway about 1945.

Hope House – Jack Powell moulding the hops in June with a Cleartrac (Cleveland, USA tractor, 1918-20).

June

Started moulding hops. Rolled and harrowed hops. Sheepshearing. Cold for whole week, bad for time of year nothing growing, frost damage everywhere. Spraying hops. Started mowing for hay. Blight very bad. All hops to have heads trained, found leaf spot. Burning hop bottoms. Working in currants. Sorting potatoes, mowing at Sevington. Bad blight sprayed hops. Finished tying hops second time and sprayed bases with tar oil. Potters' cattle been in hops. Started hopwashing. Bad thunderstorm Hope House hop kiln struck by lightning. Baled hay. Swarm of bees came. Powdered hops for nettle head (1961). Stripping hops. Mowed seeds, hoeing roots.

July

Hop training, very hot. Started to plough up old hopyard. 4 women cutting out downy mildew in hops. Started currant picking. 121 trays of currants. Whitewashing for arrival of hop pickers. Too hot to spray hops after 12 noon. Currant pickers strike for more money. Hop insurance man inspected hopyards.

Harrowing hops. Wages up to £30. 5s. (1975). Cultivating hops, found blight, all hops to be resprayed. Hop washing, hay making. 172 trays of currants. Baby lost, place in pandemonium, police involved, all had refreshments. Powdered hops with hormone. Washing hops, blight worse than expected. Mowing machine broken, baler also broken down. Hops not moving much.

August

Finish picking old currants. Started others. 253 trays. Sprayed potatoes. Currant pickers back home, working hops, plum picking. Sprayed hops for blight, remainder to currants. Sprayed hops found more blight than good. Put Bordeaux mixture on hops. Cutting corn and baling hay. 50 chips of plums to Hereford. Started hop-pickers' quarters. Gales all night and day, some hops badly affected. Cleaned hop kiln. Post in wire work broken, propped up temporarily. Blued hops. Following gale lots of strings down and cross wires. Hop-pickers arrived. Hope House, B. Cross putting sheets on barn.

September

Hop-picking good progress. Sulphured hops. Picking Goldings hot and windy. Fair first day at Hope House 144 sacks. Bagger broken, repaired bagger, bagged hops. Hops deteriorated from last Tuesday's rain. Every farmer a little worried. Beginning

Hop powderer drawn by two horses.

to understand machine (1961). Hops weighing light. Good weather, finished first hopyard light crop. Broke bagger again. Machine doing better. Very good hops from Sevington. Hops to Ledbury. Mushrooms. Sent 39 pockets to P. Pudge. Hops being very wet picked dirty. Bagger broke. Finished picking. Cutting bines. Started damson picking. Good week 4 kiln loads every day.

October

Finished drying 262 pockets. Drew money to pay hop-pickers. Finished burning bines. Moved hops to warehouse. Dismantled hop-picking machine. Pickers back to Dudley. Geo to Tenbury – hop prizes. Potatoes finished. Started apple picking. Finished thatching ricks (1954). Put 3 ton slag on hops. Geo showed hops again did well. Planting hop roots. Finished stubble ploughing. Planted wheat. Hope House hops sampled. Too wet to spray. Harvest supper at Parish Room. Muck spreading on hops. Ploughing up hops. Started getting up hop roots quite a big job but not so many as I thought, a few or more for sale.

November

Trimming hopyard hedge. Tractors all out of order. Muck on hops. Ploughing up hops. Bad wet weather. Got 500 hop roots ready for Newton Williams. Fetched 20 hop poles. Spread shoddy. To Worcester with hop roots.

'Queen Nance' at the bottom of Old Road, Bromyard, with a load of shoddy for the hopyards. The steam engine, made by John Fowler of Leeds in 1909, was a common sight round Bromyard until 1934.

December

Mucking hopyards. Topping hopyard hedge. Hop roots from R. Anthony. Redfern looking at elms with disease (1971). Finished mucking hops. Land wet. Watkins on wirework. Begin currant pruning. Hop valuation. Spray currants with tar oil, bad weather for job. Saw Watkins re hop poles. Foot and mouth at the Seed, Cradley, fetched 5 cattle in to feed from Jumpers Hole under licence. Plough up hops.

Entries for December 31:

1954	Ploughing hops Bull Ring.
1958	A remarkable season, weather almost uncanny, records broken, shocking for harvest and hop-picking. Stock did well.
1959	No hunting for quite a time. Frost – distemper – then foot and mouth.
1962	Snowed in, nothing done beside stock. Men walked to work.
1964	Hops being sampled.
1965	Wages rose to £10.10.0.
1970	Wages up to £14.16.0.
1973	Except for frost taking currants a wonderful season. Hops in plenty; also corn, hay, etc. Very open autumn.
1977	A funny year. Plenty of most things. No currant buyers.

Hopyard in winter

CHAPTER 7

Students and Shepherd's Pie

'Of all other dooings house keeping is cheefe.'

Thomas Tusser, 1524?-1580.

The establishment of the picking machine in the mid-1960s caused infinite regret to many people, but surely sighs of relief were heaved by farmers' wives and families. Life must be easier for them than during hand-picking days now that more depends on a well-regulated machine and less on unpredictable hungry human beings. However, for the high quality crops wanted by the brewers today, hops have to be harvested at the peak of their condition. This means working for the maximum number of hours during that time, and Gwenllian Paske of Upper Lyde, writing in 1988, begins her account of how hop-picking affected the farm-house with sentiments remarkably familiar:

'September – once one is a hop farmer's wife that month will never seem the same again. For it is in September that hop picking happens – a hectic period of 2½-4 weeks.

On our farm a two-shift system was started recently and involves commenc-ing at 6 a.m. and going on till 1 a.m. With a 19-hour day, it means that some workers need to start very early if on the 6 a.m. to 3.30 p.m. shift, and much later if on the second shift, 3.30 p.m. to 1 a.m. As all jobs are duplicated, except in the kiln, more workers are needed. There were not enough locally, so the solution has been to employ students. They are accommodated in caravans hired for the "picking". Our hop farm is not situated, as some farms are, very near to a catering pub for these students – about twenty – to have a pub lunch or any meals. A possible option could have been a shop offering various provisions, but we decided after all to provide all meals.

The thought of providing the students' meals, meals for the three kiln men and not forgetting the family, did seem overwhelming at first. Panic – but then an important part of the hop farmer's wife's make-up, placidness and adaptability, were drawn on. A timetable was the first item to be arranged. Gradually everything then fell into place, type of meal, extra plates and cutlery needed, etc., etc. How fortunate that the School Meals Service was drastically cut back just then!

Preparations for hop picking in September begin early in the year in spring-time – the work force, who is available? For the students, advertisements are placed in student magazines or notices are sent to maybe an agricultural college to be pinned on their notice board for holiday jobs. You just sit back then and hope that the short time with good rates of pay will attract.

Nearer September detailed planning goes on. The supplier of the caravans, the milkman for extra milk, are notified, and then of course there is the menu. Actually, these menus and notes if safely kept reduce preparation and serve as guidelines for each year. During August the butcher is contacted for meat to be cut up into joints for roasting and boiling, other meat into pieces for casseroles and meat pies, and mince for shepherd's pies. All of this goes into the freezer, at least one hopes it will. Also into the freezer in August go fruit cakes and buns, and pastry for topping the popular chicken and mushroom or fruit pies.

During the week prior to hop picking is the "big shop" and this hopefully includes enough of all dry goods to take one through the period. Back home with these goods and then the dairy is full and cupboards are bursting; the cellar has never been used like this since the days before fridges. It must be remembered that during hop picking there is only minimum time for shopping.

At last, the "day before" arrives, the day for all the last-minute jobs that have been put off, e.g. is the First Aid Box complete? And in the late afternoon and evening the students should arrive. Note, I use "should arrive" as thoughts

Gwen Paske serving another meal at Upper Lyde in 1987.

Mr. and Mrs. H.N. Paske, Upper Lyde, Hereford, HR4 8AE
Telephone — Hereford 760220

Leave Hereford on A49 Leominster/Shrewsbury Road.   Pass Lyde Church
on your right after approximately 3 miles and take the next left turn
by telephone box (before Greenhous' Garage).   Proceed up lane ½ mile
(beware of bends) and first farmhouse on your right is Upper Lyde.

Arrive previous day afternoon/evening.

Hoppicking begins   at 6.00 a.m.(if possible)
Confirmation of date will be given in August.

Please bring :-   Sleeping Bag
                         Wellington Boots
                         Alarum Clock
                         Clothes for WET and COLD Weather
                         Thermos Flask

Meals are provided and there are facilities (kettle, toaster, boiling
ring) for extra snacks.

AT WEEKENDS - On Saturdays   Light lunch for early shift workers only
                             Cereal and toast available for 2nd Shift.

          On Sundays   Breakfast of cereal and toast available

1st Shift: 2nd Shift:

5.30 a.m. Breakfast   No work on Saturdays
6.00 a.m. - 9.00 a.m. Work   Breakfast - help yourself
9.00 a.m. - 9.30 a.m. Break   1.00 Dinner
          (Flask & Biscuits)   3.30 p.m. - 7.00 p.m. Work
9.30 a.m. - 12 noon   Work   7.00 p.m. - 8.00 p.m. Meal
12 noon - 1.00 p.m. Dinner   8.00 p.m. - 10.30 p.m. Work
1.00 p.m. - 3.30 p.m. Work   10.30 p.m. - 11.00 p.m. Break
3.30 p.m. - Tea (1st shift only)   (Flask and Biscuits)
                                    11.00 p.m. - 1.00 a.m. Work
Saturday - work only until
           approximately 12 noon

Wages £.......... per hour.   National Insurances contributions
                              will be deducted.

£.......... per day (5 days per week) will be deducted for keep.

P.A.Y.E. is not deducted from genuine students

Information sheet for hop pickers.

cross your mind, did they receive the information sheet sent out three weeks earlier? Perhaps they have decided not to come after all, the girlfriend wants Tim to go elsewhere, and then the telephone rings, "I am at Hereford Station, can someone come and meet me?" Soon after, a bright coloured jalopy arrives and I relax once again, there will be some workers! At last to bed, my husband and I each with an alarm clock!

The day of the start, and 5.15 a.m. the alarm goes off. The early shift are woken up, breakfast smells come from the welcoming warm kitchen and the first pot of tea of the day is made. Not much conversation is needed at this time, just instructions! The first breakfast is over, the students, quite likely dressed in warm clothes, and the hopyard gang with their flasks, climb onto trolleys and are off to gather the first bines. Other workers go to the machine to work there, and the "rattlings" from the machine start up as the motors are switched on and the various tracks go into motion.

For me, there is such relief to have reached this stage, to have started "hopping". Obviously, I have to have extra help in the house for preparation of vegetables (the saucepan for potatoes is so large that it seems the bottom will never be covered), telephone calls and messages (although the cordless telephone helps considerably here), some cleaning that must be done regularly

Load of hops in front of the old kilns at Upper Lyde with a cowl showing above the pockets and the old greenstage (space for stacking greensacks) at the rear.

(most important in washing and toilet places) and of course the dishwasher can't take all the washing up.

Home nursing is needed at times, if only for dealing with a nasty cut that may mean a stitch at the local hospital.

Mealtimes keep coming and with an element of luck on your side everyone seems satisfied. Gradually, one learns the likes and dislikes. How nice it is to remember the person's name when passing them their meal – but that is being hopeful in the first days! Then one finds that in the dairy there is room to move groceries around, the freezer will shut properly, there is only one pack of toilet paper left!

At last, when cutlery, plates, etc., are packed away, chairs are really clean, one contemplates rather wearily, that's enough for this year, next year will come round soon enough!'

Robert Maund stacks the greenstage at Panks Bridge Farm in 1968.

CHAPTER 8

Hop Kilns

'Some skilfullie drieth their hops on a kell,
and some on a soller, oft turning them well.
Kell dried will abide, foule weather or faire,
where drieng and lieng in loft doo dispaire.'

Thomas Tusser, 1524?-1580.

Hops must be carefully dried and special buildings have been developed for this purpose; in Herefordshire these are known as hop kilns, but in other areas they are termed oasthouses. An early method of drying was to spread the green hops on an upper floor or in an attic and allow them to dry naturally. In his book, *A Perfite Platforme of a Hoppe Garden* published in 1574, Reynolde Scot describes such a method: 'If you have no Oast dry them in a loft open to the air as maybe lay them not above half a foot thick and turn them once a day at the least, by the space of two or three weeks sweep them up into a corner let them lay for as long more.' Some local growers without kilns were using Scot's method as late as the 19th century, whilst others took their hops to be dried by neighbours; eventually most hop growers built their own kilns. In 1842, for example, there were 23 farms in Stoke Lacy growing hops, of which at least 14 are known to have had kilns or to have built them later.

All kilns use the principle of rising hot air to dry the crop. A slatted wooden floor, 2.4 to 3 metres (8 to 10 feet) above a smokeless fire, is covered with a woven horsehair cloth on which the green hops are spread in a thin layer. Early Herefordshire kilns were described as being similar to malt kilns, and were probably used for either task. In 1793 it was stated that Kentish kilns had been 'lately introduced' to the county. These were of the hopper type, having a small brick fireplace about a metre square, beneath an inverted lath and plaster cone which funnelled the hot air to the drying floor above, sometimes as large as 3.7 metres square (12 feet square). Brockmanton Hall, Puddlestone, advertised for sale in 1805, had 'Six excellent Kentish Hop-kilns, newly erected at considerable expense'. Later, brick vaulting replaced the lath and plaster hopper and small ventilators were fixed on the ridge of the roof, allowing the hot air to escape. Kilns of this type were housed in a low, two-storey, ridge-roofed building, often adjoining the house, and with access between house and kiln on both floors. A few of these hopper kilns still survive locally.

The round brick kiln, with a tall tapering roof capped by a cowl that swings with the wind, was in use in Kent by 1815. In Herefordshire these were rare before the 1840s and became quickly outmoded, although a few were built as late as the 1880s.

Both round and square kilns were frequently added to the gable of a cider house (as at Little Cowarne Court), creating the combined cider house/hop kiln which became the standard arrangement on most hop-growing farms. Towards the end of the 19th century a pair of square kilns could be linked under a single roof, as at Wolferlow Court.

Lath and plaster hopper kilns at Lower Elmores End, Whitbourne.

The introduction of forced draught to improve the venting of moist air reduced the need for tall cones with cowls. Lower (and cheaper) roofs with louvred caps became common and, when linked under one roof, evolved into full-length louvred ridge ventilation. This was easily adaptable for large scale operations.

Drying

All hop drying depends on warm, dry air rising from a heat source through a bed of hops, and escaping above it through cowls, louvres or other forms of vent. The initial temperature must be allowed to increase only slowly otherwise a moisture laden 'reek' from the lower layers will condense onto upper layers which are still cool, giving them a dull appearance and lowering their value. The main skill of the drier is in knowing just when to stop drying. The bracts, or petals, will be dry and the strig at the centre of the cone will retain just enough moisture for it to remain

Hopper kilns at Lower Elmores End, Whitbourne. Two kilns inserted perhaps in the late 18th or early 19th century, into an earlier timber-framed building. The timber and plaster hopper above the fireplace minimises fire risk. These kilns are now taken down.   *Jennifer Weale*

A cowl mounted on a pitched roof, formerly at Ankerdine Farm (see end of Chapter 12 for aerial view of farm).

tough. After removal from the kiln hops need to be confined in a heap to allow the moisture to redistribute itself into the bracts, making them more supple again and less liable to damage. These factors have been borne in mind during the development of all systems of drying, from the open fire system to the most modern.

In the days of the anthracite fires, the hop driers were very skilled and trusted men. The fires had to be kept at an even red glow all the time which entailed stoking, probably every half-hour, night and day. Thermometers displayed the temperature of each kiln and these had to be watched carefully for any change. The head drier also had to know the exact time to unload the hops, judged by the feel, smell and general condition of the hops. As it was a twenty-four hour job there were usually at least two driers who took it in turn to tend the fires, but both were needed to unload the kiln during the night as this entailed moving a large volume of hops. Extra labour was often available during the day for loading, when the head drier would be in charge and rake the hops to the required depth on the kiln floor, while the other men brought in greensacks, on their backs, and emptied them where directed.

The driers had their own rooms for resting and had their short sleeps on a palliasse stuffed with straw. When on duty they had to keep awake; the drier in charge at Cradley Hall Farm in the early '30s, Sidney Box, a well-known local man of strong radical opinions, kept a bottle hanging from the ceiling in the kiln so that if he nodded off he knocked himself against it and woke up. Others chose to sit in a wheelbarrow when on duty (with handles on the ground) so that if they dropped off to sleep the wheelbarrow would tip and they would wake up. The driers' room was often quite a social centre in the evenings with locals calling in for a chat and to hear how the picking was progressing, bringing news from other farms and general gossip. A game of darts was the popular pastime on these occasions and some visitors would stay on to help with changing the kilns. The local policemen also used to come round from time to time. In most cases the driers' week finished in the early hours of Sunday morning when they went home and then had to be on duty again mid-day on Monday.

After the hops have been dried they have to be tightly packed into large, strong, jute sacks or pockets, each pocket measuring 6 feet by 3 feet and holding about 1½ cwt of hops when full. The hops are compressed in this manner partly for transport, but mainly for storage as when tightly packed they will keep for long periods. The method of packing the hops into the pockets remained the same in many places until the late 19th century. A round bagging or treading hole, of which many local examples still exist, was cut in the upper floor of a hop room or farmhouse and a hoop slightly larger than the hole was sewn in the mouth of the pocket, which was then passed down through the hole and suspended by the hoop. In later years, the open end of

Linton Brook around 1910. The service wing contained the hop-drying kiln, and the louvres for the hot air to escape can be seen on the ridge of the roof.

A small hop-drying unit at Little Cowarne Court in use until 1959.

LITTLE COWARNE COURT HOP KILNS

The original 16th or 17th century stone building, known as the Mill after the cider mill, is a good example of the way farm buildings have been adapted over the years. The west end has a fine fireplace and may have been the original farmhouse with a granary above. The 18th century hop drying unit probably consisted of a pair of kilns against the east end of the building in the area now taken up by the cider mill, and the granary was also used as a hop room for cooling and bagging. The old hop treading holes have been boarded over and nowadays traces can only be detected from below. The brick hop kilns of c1880 are unusual in having brick cones instead of the more customary slate or tile hung roofs of Herefordshire. The bricks were baked on the farm by Thomas Fletcher of Rose Cottage, Little Cowarne; building round kilns would have been no problem for a bricklayer used to sinking brick-lined wells. The cones were waterproofed with pitch and the pointed cowls protected by lead tips. An extractor fan was added to improve the draught – see illustration above left with William Pearson standing beside its engine in 1956. The furnace in its later form was fired with anthracite and never converted to oil fuel; similarly, the hand-driven press was never converted to power. The bunk space was for the drier who had to live on the job during hop picking.

the pocket was turned over the hoop which then fitted onto a flange surrounding the bagging hole. A telling description of the operation occurs in E. J. Lance's *The Hop Farmer* published in 1838:

> 'The hops are tramped into these bags by a man, while a boy supplies him from a basket and it will take 3 to 4 hours to tramp each bag, and to tramp 4 bags @ 9d is a very good day's work for a man. In treading the man becomes covered in yellow dust; it nearly chokes the man and he must be supplied with beer to keep his throat clear.'

In Herefordshire, the drink could also have been cider or perry, but the job was just as dusty for most local treading holes were placed near a door to gain as much light and air as possible. After the pocket was full, the hoop was removed and the pocket lowered to the floor below where it was sewn up and weighed, the weight being stencilled on the side. In the first half of the 19th century the hop press had been invented, a mechanical device to pack hops into a pocket without the need for a man to go down into it. It contained a plunger that could be rammed into the pocket by multiple gearing, then withdrawn for more hops to be added and forced down again and again until the pocket was full. This could be between 9 and 13 times depending on how well the hops were weighing. The early hop presses were hand-operated but today they have all been converted to power. Most farms now have 'balers' which are powered by a hydraulic ram and require only 2 or 3 presses per bale, speeding up the operation considerably.

Twin kilns in brick, added to an earlier stone cider house at Wolferlow Court.
Joan Grundy

Low-roofed kilns with flat caps for ventilation, at St. Donat's Farm, Burghill. The two nearer kilns have stovepipes for venting combustion fumes.   *Joan Grundy*

The hop kiln on the left was built at Wicton, Bredenbury by landowner H. J. Bailey of Rowden Abbey and is dated 'H J B Diamond Jubilee 1897'. By 1916, hops were no longer grown in the parish.

A succession of ridge-vented kilns dating from 1926 to 1973, inserted into earlier buildings. The earliest, on the left, occupies the end bay of a timber-framed barn and has in the far gable a round opening for a top fan – compare with photograph on p.152.

Joan Grundy

The Hop Kilns, Suckley was originally a bank of six kilns around a three storey stowage. This building type occurs frequently in Kent and is also seen in the Teme valley, but is uncommon in Herefordshire. It was devised to avoid mixing green and dried hops, which can happen when the cooling floor is also the loading floor, as is usual in early kilns. Here, the green hops are hoisted by horse pulley to the top floor for loading the kilns, and dried hops are drawn out onto the cooling floor beneath. The filled hop pockets are stored at ground level.   *Joan Grundy*

The hop kilns at New House, Stretton Grandison well illustrate the fortunes of the Herefordshire hop industry in the 19th and 20th centuries. Around the 1840s, a pair of round brick kilns with slate roofs were added at the end of a stone cider house, using the granary as a cooling room. A drawing dated 1869 shows the cowls and vanes. The square kiln with cowl was added before 1904. Next, one of the round kilns was pulled down and the bricks reused, with new bricks, in the building of a second square kiln. Perhaps at the same time a wide loading door was made into the cooling room and the greenstage added (now partially removed). The two kilns on the right had top fans installed to improve draught, the cowls being replaced by louvred caps. On the extreme left is the corner of the hop-picking machine shed. A ridge-vented kiln (left of the square kilns) was built in 1980 and the cooling floor extended. Hops were last dried here in 1987, and last harvested on the estate in 2004. (With acknowledgement to Mr. Brian Willder, Farm Manager, for dates and details.)

Joan Grundy

Walter Dew stoking the kiln fire at Upper Lyde. The horseshoe is for lighting the sulphur.

Walter Dew levelling hops – note the unguarded belt for the extractor fan in the background.

A lifter hair in a kiln at Stanford Court. The early hairs were permanently fastened down and the hops pushed out with a hop shovel.

The hops in a pile for the moisture to be redistributed before being bagged.

The very old fashioned way, 'treading' them in.

Operating a press by hand and using a 'scuppet' to push the hops. The open end-flaps of the pocket were pulled over a ring, similar to the one on the wall, before the pocket was lowered into the bagging hole.

Similar press converted to power assisted. The handle controlled a clutch.   *Brian Willder*

Richard Potter stands beside a full pocket suspended below the press. Three generations of Gladys Draper's family have helped with the hops at Stanford Court, and before the press was installed her grandmother, Mrs. Hill of Shobdon Cottage, not only worked on hop tying and picking but trod hops there as well.

Pockets ready to go to the warehouse. Rosemaund Farm, Felton.

Joan Grundy

Kiln tools at Stanford Court: two square wooden shovels or scuppets, with an older round-headed one on the right; a wide rake; and a wooden fork with extra tines. Also in the picture are two balls of hop string; a bundle of hop pegs; a pole-puller's pole; and an old stencil for marking the pockets.

Hop driers and their tools outside a Madley kiln in 1901: wooden scuppets; a pan of roll sulphur; perhaps charks in a sieve; a pocket still with its sack hooks and the bagger with his strings for sewing it up, while the bowler-hatted farmer records the weight of his crop.

Pockets of dried hops being loaded at Felton Court in 1933.

A good load of pockets. (Let's hope there were no low bridges!)

CHAPTER 9

The Hop Grower's Year

'The hop joyeth in a fat and fruitful ground: also it groweth among briers and thornes about the borders of fields, I meane the wilde kind.'

John Gerard, 1545-1612.

Since the Second World War the methods and productivity of British agriculture have probably altered and improved more than during any equivalent time span, and in the following calendars Harry Paske explains the differences that have occurred in hop growing. The system described before 1950 is as he remembers it at Little Froome. Hop growing was given up there in 1964 so he has described his own system at Upper Lyde for the 1980s.

The methods are peculiar to the periods and to the individual farms. No two hop growers ever had the same ideas or did things in the same way, and no two hop growers ever will, but the changes depicted are generally representative of the whole industry.

BEFORE MACHINE PICKING
(Pre 1950)

October

After hop picking, the bines remained lying in the hopyard; many would not have been severed from the stock. All would be cut back to a few inches and tumped into alternate rows until dry enough to burn. This left the other rows free for loads of farmyard manure to be tipped into heaps for spreading when the bines were burnt.

MACHINE PICKING
(1985-6)

October

Earlier picking and the cutting of the bines for harvest, means we no longer rush in to cut off the remnants of the bines, but leave them on an extra month, so that the few remaining leaves can provide a certain amount of sustenance for the future. Ground pegs unprotected by the soil with which we used to smother the weeds will need straightening and replacing, so as not to hinder cutting next month. We no longer use farmyard manure.

Frequent use of tractors produces 'no-go' areas for roots and a subsoiler is drawn through the ground just inside the wheel marks to shatter the offending barrier. The high hedges are trimmed.

Diseased and surplus hops are grubbed with a tool originally designed by CWS Farms to lift their rhubarb stocks.

November   *(Pre 1950)*

After the FYM was spread the soil was ploughed up to the hops from the middle of the rows. This exposed the furrows to the frost, helping to create a tilth for next season and also, if the yard was suitably situated, helping rain to run off.

Ground for new yards was ploughed, cultivated level and the positions for new plants marked out with ground pegs.

November   *(1985-6)*

All surface hop growth has usually died off by the end of the second week and we are free to cut off the remnants of bine to ground level, ready for tumping up and burning when dry enough. Now that the crop is dormant it is safe to spray herbicides. Often, however, conditions are not good enough until March or April.

Areas for planting are ploughed if necessary and prepared with a power-driven harrow with reciprocating tines ready for marking out with ground pegs.

December

Poles and wirework were checked and repairs and renewals made where necessary.

If new hop setts were not available from home-grown cuttings, they were bought privately or at Ledbury Hop Root Sale in November, and planted out when soil conditions were suitable.

December

Repairs and renewals are carried out to the wirework. The hop-picking machine is serviced by skilled fitters.

Hop roots, certified virus free, are planted out.

January

New wirework was erected over the newly planted setts. Hedges were trimmed with hedgebills using ladders or standing on trailers where necessary. Ditches were cleaned and broken drains repaired. Prunings from the apple orchards were hauled to a convenient position to be available for hop pickers to collect for firewood in September.

January

Wirework is erected over young hops. If the land has been fallowed or rested from hops for two years, the wirework would not have been removed. Ditches are cleaned and drainage faults corrected. Yards are walked and dead stocks replaced.

Watkins and Griffiths also trim the high hedges surrounding the yards with a rotating flail hedge trimmer. This job we dare not do when the crop is growing. The anchor wires supporting the wirework tend to be hidden by leaves in the summer, and it is much too easy to accidentally sever a wire when it is under the tension of the weight of the crop, and a considerable collapse could then take place.

Burning bine. Norah Wheale at Upper Lyde.

Trimming a hopyard hedge.

February   *(Pre 1950)*

Wireworking was finished off, and top-hooks fixed to the parallel wires by operators using a long, pruner-like tool.

The ground is usually at its wettest during this month, but if conditions were unusually good a start could be made with spring operations.

March

The soil was ploughed from the hops back to the middle of the rows. Then the throwing down and cutting was done. Soil between the plants was removed by handwork with kerfs or three-pronged Canterbury hoes. The hops were then cut back to the crown using cranked cutting hooks. Good, healthy, strong cuttings would be selected from the debris for planting in a nursery for use as replacements the following year or even for gapping up in the current year. Damaged pegs were straightened or replaced. Except for the bigger growers, most farmers kept enough men to manage these jobs without casual labour at that time of year.

The first dressings of artificial fertilizer were applied if the weather allowed.

February   *(1985-6)*

Wirework and top-hook replacement is completed.

The increased area of hops and decreased labour force make it necessary to start stringing hops this month or more casual labour will have to be employed in April. Under the old system of cultivating, the stringing could not go ahead anyway until the ploughing, throwing down and cutting had been done, so that the ground pegs were uncovered and could be put right to take the string.

March

As no cultivating work is to be done, when conditions are dry enough it is possible to catch up with any weed control spraying left over from the autumn. This needs to be done as soon as practicable so that unfolding leaves are not damaged.

Phosphate and potash fertilizer will be spread if the opportunity arises.

Martin Hewitt pegging at Panks Bridge Farm, Much Cowarne in 1968. Graeham Davies stringing in the background.

April *(Pre 1950)*

The ground was cultivated when conditions were suitable, to level it off, as much as to kill weeds. Plants that had died were dug out and replaced.

Stringing had to be done in good time, as plants that were growing across the ground when they should be climbing the strings were very difficult to tie late and would be very slow to grow anyway. Regular labour would do the job on a piecework basis. Old Jim Walton had done the job for so many years that even when he could no longer see the top-hooks he was able to have a very creditable go at it.

Women did the next job – bracing the hop strings together with binder twine. This prevented them hanging loosely into the alleys to be snagged by traffic. At Little Froome a regular gang of up to a dozen women under the control of Elsie Bridgewater from the Ballhurst used to start the season with this job, following on with hop tying by the end of the month. For this the best shoots, not necessarily the strongest and coarsest or those produced from long runners which tended to kink off later on, were trained clockwise round the string. The unwanted bines were ripped out by hand leaving two to grow up each string or perhaps two up one and three up the other in case one happened to perish.

May

The tying gang would go over a second time to attend to the weaker shoots and correct any bines that had heads entangled with each other, or which were climbing the wrong strings. Spiky heads infected with downy mildew would be picked and burnt, and Bordeaux powder applied as a preventive.

Cultivation and rolling continued as necessary to remove weeds, level the ground and create tilth. A second dressing of fertilizer was applied.

April *(1985-6)*

A fungicide against mould is sprayed at least twice.

Stringing will be finished, the strings no longer being braced together, except at the end of the rows where it is necessary to prevent snagging by tractors when turning in.

Tying starts sometime after the 20th of the month. Here again the rules have been altered. The hop tiers' instructions are to see that at least three bines are furnished to each string. On no account are surplus bines to be removed unless there is no other way of furnishing the adjacent string with the right quantity. The basal growth is not to be removed and no time to be wasted by treading down unwanted bines.

Ground from which hops were grubbed last October and November will be cultivated as time and weather allow to keep free of weeds, and also to prepare a tilth ready for when the soil is warm enough in June or July to be injected with a soil sterilant.

May

The gang of five or six hop tiers will go twice round our forty acres and then two people will be sufficient to reposition any heads that stray from their predestined path, unless a period of quick growth is accompanied by strong gales which cause a great deal of havoc.

Clear polythene tubes, three to four foot long, are slipped over weak hops before the first defoliant spray of diluted tar oil is applied to kill off unwanted bottom growth.

Nettles and couch grass must be sprayed with a knapsack sprayer, and docks dug out by hand.

According to the soil analysis more phosphate or potash fertilizer may be applied. The first dressing of nitrogen will go on this month.

Fungicides will be sprayed at fortnightly intervals for the rest of the season.

Stringing from stilts – Alan Morris hand tying the tops; someone would follow closely behind dibbing the bottom end into the ground close to the stock. A difficult job on a windy day!

Charlie Phillips stringing the Front Hopyard at Little Froome in the early 1950s. The string is carried in the bag and guided from peg to hook by the 'monkey', a long rod with a tube attached to the end.

June   *(Pre 1950)*

The tying gang returned to leaf the hops.

Damson-hop aphid always appeared in June when the populations became too dense on the damson and blackthorn and had to migrate to the hop. Sprays or 4% nicotine dust were used. Hops were still walked and treated against downy and powdery mildews. By the middle of June, hops were expected to reach the top wire – it was then only 12 feet high – and the last nitrogen was applied (any later and there was a danger of hops being devalued for being too green).

Cultivations were carried out with scuffles, spring tines or discs, not only to kill weeds but to create a good depth of mould or tilth that was then ploughed over the base of the hops to smother weeds and encourage basal swelling to form good, strong cuttings.

At Little Froome any spare time from other farm duties in June was occupied by riding in a horse-drawn cart down the rows correcting heads that had fallen back from the strings because of the wind or other causes. In good growing weather a bine might grow a foot in twenty-four hours and a sudden change to windy weather could cause it to fall back before it had time to develop a grip on the string.

June   *(1985-6)*

Because hop aphid usually appears during the first week of June, a measured dose of cytrolane spray is applied to each stock electronically. The tractor driver has to press the button 62,320 times so his thumb gets a little sore!

The last nitrogen will probably be applied, but if slow growth continues it may be put on as late as July, now that green hop samples are not frowned on as they used to be.

Hop heads are now out of reach from the ground, unless the workers are able to use forked sticks to control the recalcitrants by catching the heads and twisting them round the string. Unfortunately most people have insufficient co-ordination to do this without breaking off many of the heads, and if we are in real trouble with displacement a tractor fitted with a platform is used so the operation can be done by hand.

Progressive wilt starts to appear on infected farms from July. We take delivery of the diesel fuel used for drying in June and have sufficient storage capacity for the whole season. The risk of wilt transference is extremely great on farms where storage is limited and deliveries may have to be made as often as twice a week during picking. Tankers travelling from farm to farm drive over the same paths as any wilted hops that may be coming in to the picking machines and could transfer this infected material to other farms.

Fallowed soil will be injected with a sterilant.

Bracing the strings by tying them together with cut lengths of binder twine is no longer economic unless rows are so narrow that snagging from implements occurs. Upper Lyde.

July   *(Pre 1950)*

Cultivations were continued to suppress weeds. Aphids had to be destroyed at least once in the month and fungicides were included in the spray mix. Red spider mite was no problem because the systemic insecticides then in use were also extremely efficient acaricides. If downy mildew was still a problem the spike had to be removed, because if downy was not got rid of by the middle of the month there was trouble as it could destroy the developing burr (flower). If mould was still present the tying gang would have to return to strip off any regrowth of leaves on the lower bine.

Plants with the virus diseases nettlehead or mosaic were dug out, together with adjacent stocks in order to remove latent infection.

Hops being sprayed against aphid. Note the driver, T. Wheale, is wearing full protective clothing. Upper Lyde.

July   *(1985-6)*

The crop will have reached the top wire by the beginning of July and will start coming into burr about the middle of the month. Males are in a ratio of 1:200 and wind is the pollinating agent. Hops will develop from the burr without pollination but the crop won't be so heavy.

Fallen bines need restringing frequently, to prevent damage by hopyard traffic.

Red spider mite must be watched for in hot, dry periods.

From now on yards must be systematically and thoroughly walked at least once every week so that every single plant has been seen, and if the slightest suspicion of wilt is observed (evidenced by total dying of the plant), the Ministry of Agriculture will be immediately informed. When looking for wilt I do not consider any other pest or disease whatsoever: it is so important to spot any infection immediately that there must be no distraction. Looking for normal pests is an entirely different operation.

Perry Pudge operating the hop powdering machine that he developed to mount on a Fordson tractor in the early 1920s.

August   *(Pre 1950)*

It was still important to clear up the weeds because of the hop pickers in September. Fat hen was remarkably uncomfortable to walk through when wet, even if one was properly dressed for the occasion, and the annual nettle (Urtica urens) which seems to be more common in hopyards than anywhere else in this part of the country, although only half the size of the common stoloniferous variety has at least twice the stinging power.

Fungicidal dust was blown on the crop if necessary, but if a late fly-in of aphids occurred a complete spray mix was applied by the Three Counties Sprayers.

Preparations for hop picking began. Cribs were brought out of storage, torn cloths sewn up and broken timbers repaired. The kilns were cleared of all potatoes, fruit, corn, small dead animals and lost tools that had accumulated over the year. If the heating pipes hadn't been cleaned (and they usually hadn't), they had to be attended to. It was particularly important to clean the outside chimneys – one had exploded at Little Froome due to a dead owl being jammed in a bend. The kiln equipment – motors, fans, baggers, were all checked and lubricated. Greensacks and kiln hairs were repaired and the hop pockets obtained. Clean straw was stuffed into green sacks to make beds for the kiln staff.

Hubert Baker, the council roadman, was contacted to confirm that he could have time off from the council once more to do the hop drying. Adam Jones, who did a lot of contract sheepshearing, had to be contacted in case bending over sheep had crippled him, and he would no longer be able to do the bushelling. It never did and he always could. An advertisement for hop pickers and sometimes for a booker had to be placed in the Bromyard paper. Bank staff on holiday were viewed warily because a bank manager had once stood in for his son for a day and the arithmetical mistakes he had made had caused a lot of trouble.

August   *(1985-6)*

On most varieties burr will develop into full hop during this month and picking could possibly start during the last week.

In order to examine the crop thoroughly it is necessary to use a ladder as plants that are otherwise clean can have pests and diseases hidden in the top growth which cannot possibly be seen from the ground. Any problem patches would need to be picked earlier as ignorance of their presence could lead to the development of a completely unsaleable mess.

Last minute servicing of the hop-picking machine, hop-drying burners, kiln equipment and bine hauling equipment will be carried out. Lastly the kilns will be swept out – an Augean task if they have been used for corn drying, because of the vast quantities of dust that will have been deposited throughout.

Hopyard at Upper Lyde in midsummer with the house and new kilns on the skyline.

September   *(Pre 1950)*

Fuggle hops of the best value were usually picked on about September 25th and this was borne in mind when deciding when to start. Fuggles were the only hops grown at Little Froome. Other factors had to be considered of course, such as ripeness of the hops and how long the picking was likely to last. A few days before the appointed one, the cribs were placed on the headland of the yard where the start was to be made, and all was ready.

Whether natural early risers or not, the pickers arrived early on the first day to ensure they could have cribs to their liking. Pole pullers, so called because their job originally consisted of pulling down the poles for the hops to be picked in the days before wirework, would carry the cribs into the 'houses' to be picked. They had the impossible task of working out a rational system of moving cribs forward into the yard so that no picker could complain of having small hops to pick all the time. No system was good enough to quell all complaints, particularly from the less industrious who were not to be moved until they had tidied the space round their cribs and picked all the loose hops off the ground. Yard staff quickly developed skins of pachydermal impermeability which were only rarely punctured sufficiently to elicit retaliation.

September   *(1985-6)*

Although the area of hops in England has decreased, the size of the average hop unit has increased and we are no exception. In spite of mechanisation, this still means that we have to begin picking earlier and, indeed, pick hops that thirty years ago the trade would have considered too green. Fortunately trade preferences have altered regarding colour, although we may be sacrificing a certain amount of yield and alpha-acid if we start too early. Consistently early picking causes serious depletion in rootstock food reserves so we have to 'ring the changes' each year with the choice of which yard to pick first.

Nowadays, the optimum time to pick hops at Upper Lyde is usually the first three weeks in September: it is very difficult, although by no means impossible, to keep hops to a sufficiently high standard to be worth picking afterwards. Two shifts per day are worked, and two twenty foot square kilns, each of three tiers gives us ample capacity to deal with the drying and bagging. Apart from the drier and two or three men in the kiln, approximately twenty people are employed on each shift, about half of them students. Four or five work in the hopyard.

Bushelling at Little Froome. Sid Taylor, Harry Paske, Janet Cook, Walter Lloyd, Adam Jones and Michael Paske.

September (continued)   *(Pre 1950)*

Three times a day Adam Jones, the busheller, would shout, 'Clear 'em up' and clamber round the hopyard, measuring the hops with the cane basket, out of the cribs and into the greensacks. The booker entered the amount picked onto the picker's card and also into the housebook kept for a check, and the pole pullers held open, tied, and loaded the full green sacks onto the tractor-drawn trailer to be taken to the kilns. Here the two kilnmen carried and tipped them onto the horse-hair covered drying floor for Hubert Baker to fluff up and level off with a fork. Kiln loading finished, roll sulphur was weighed and ignited with a red hot horseshoe in the sulphur pans below the hops. (The amount of sulphur would be later adjusted on the advice of the hop factor when he examined a dried sample.) The fans were started, the automatic stokers put into operation, and ten to twelve hours later the three kilnmen would remove the dried hops on the carrier hairs and tip them in a heap in the cooling room.

September (continued)   *(1985-6)*

The hop bines are cut with a hook three or four feet above ground level by a man (or woman) in front of the tractor and trailer. The ends are grabbed by two people on the front of the trailer as it moves through, and the bines are then severed from the top wires by a man with a hook standing on a 'crow's nest' frame temporarily fixed on the back. He has to be pretty lively to cut bines from both sides as the trailer moves forward, without being decapitated by the cross wires. Although such an accident is a possibility it has never happened yet. In fact a careless operator would be more likely to carry out such an operation with his own hook. It is always necessary to warn the hopyard gang of the danger of the cutting hooks – if this warning is ever neglected on the first day of hop picking someone invariably has to be taken to the casualty department for stitching up during the opening hours of the season.

Three tractor drivers are employed driving hops to the picking machine. Here the bines are pushed into clamps which carry them through three banks of rotating plucker fingers which strip away the cones. The resulting mixture of hop and leaf is separated by a strong air current which sucks out the leaves; the hops are further improved by passing over cascades of inclined belts which allow them to roll down and waste materials to be carried over the top. Two or three of the older ladies of the staff, who are much more efficient than anyone else at the job, remove the remaining rubbish before the hops are elevated to the top floor of the kiln and deposited in bins ready for drying.

Polepuller cutting 'flags'. Bob Baker, in Church Orchard hopyard, Little Cowarne.

Using a 'crow's nest' to reach the bines. Brian Edwards. Upper Lyde.

Feeding the hop-picking machine. Frank Price and Eric Stokes. Upper Lyde.

September (continued)   *(Pre 1950)*

Once the building was warm, Little Froome had sufficient room to store the hops for two days before putting them into the pockets. This enabled the residual moisture to redistribute itself in the hop cones, so that they changed from the brittle, dry hop immediately after drying, to acquire a soft, silky feel that enabled them to be scuppered across the floor into the hole where the pocket was suspended, without suffering any damage from shattering. One man pushed the hops up to the bagger, one turned the bagger handle which was geared well down so that the press exerted a consolidating pressure on the hops, and Hubert Baker kept an eye on the pocket from down below and sewed up and weighed it on completion. The pockets, which were marked with consecutive numbers, were all kept on the premises until after harvest, but all those with a number ending in a 5 were put on one side for priority delivery to the warehouse. This was because the Hop Marketing Board needed them to obtain 'type' samples to assist in valuation of the crop and would not pay out the first instalment of payment until all '5s' had been delivered.

Hops were picked on five days a week if the weather was good: very few pickers would brave very wet weather which was just as well because of the mess that would be caused by the hopyard traffic. If harvest was behindhand picking was done on Sundays when more than usual would be picked because of extra people from Bromyard who would be available. In some late seasons Little Froome pickers would be augmented when Tos Adams at Avenbury Court finished, or vice versa if Little Froome finished first.

September (continued)   *(1985-6)*

The hop drier and kiln men take over now. The loaded bins are pushed into the drying chamber. These are built with perforated platten bottoms which open to release the hops to a central drying floor. This is also built with perforated plattens. These open to release the hops into nylon mesh bins immediately above the plenum chamber into which the centrifugal fans of the burners force the hot air. When fully in operation three tiers of hops are thus being dried with the same hot air simultaneously. Each batch has about seven to nine hours drying time.

When the hops are dry, two men tip them out of the nylon bins into a heap for moisture redistribution to take place. The bagger is an old hand machine, now electrically powered by an apparatus built by the late Harold Edwards of Collington, and presses hops into the still conventional 'pockets'. As we have insufficient storage the pockets are sent into Ledbury warehouse as soon as a load is ready. Nowadays we use our own transport in order to lessen the chance of picking up wilt from lorries that have been hauling from infected farms. So far we have been able to choose a route that avoids driving past infected farms but that will soon be impossible because of the way the disease is spreading.

Removing leaf and string from the hops. Upper Lyde.

Walter Dew, a hop drier from an old Bromyard family, is levelling off hops
being tipped on to the drying floor of the kiln by his son. Note the carrying
hairs hooked on to the walls, which were unhooked to remove the dried hops.
Upper Lyde.

Dried hops being scuppered into the pocket for compression by the electrically-driven plunger. The motor and controls in the box were made by Harold Edwards of Collington in the '50s. Nowadays the open wheel would have to be guarded. Tom Wheale and Michael Dew. Upper Lyde.

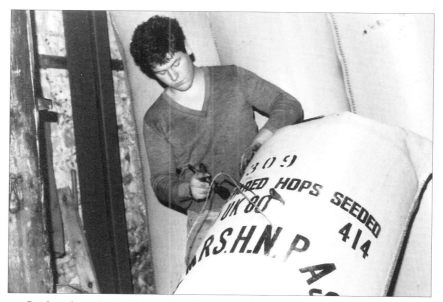

Pockets have had to be numbered consecutively since 1800. EEC regulations decree additional markings which are applied with a stencil. Norman Paske, Upper Lyde.

Each pocket of hops is weighed. A constant weight is an indication of good drying management. Michael Dew. Upper Lyde.

Loading hop pockets on to lorry at Stanford Court, Stanford Bishop.

CHAPTER 10

Servicing the Hop Industry

About 800 United Kingdom farmers grew hops in the '50s, but by 2005 the number was down to less than 121 in England, so implement makers for the hop industry have not had the benefit of large scale production as have other sectors of farming. In the early days of the tractor, however, general farm cultivating implements, having been designed for horses, were small enough to travel hop rows anyway and only slight alterations to the hitching arrangements were necessary. Ransomes of Ipswich used to make special hop ploughs and heavy disc cultivators, and Craven of Evesham were among the first makers of dusting and spraying equipment in the days of the horse. The main local suppliers of specific hop equipment used to be Wargent Brothers of Stoke Edith (later with Morris, Wargent and Wilde at Whitestone), Ted Wargent of Canon Frome, John Hill of Ledbury and Pettifer of Bromyard. They provided everything the growers needed from complete hop kilns to the steel ground pegs required by each root for the application of the coir yarn for the hops to climb. Cutting 18 inch lengths of ¼-inch steel rod and forming the hooks was a steady, time consuming job for when business was slack. Each acre required about 1800 pegs.

Pettifer of Bromyard gave up the hop part of the business in the 1960s, and Tony Winwood, a carpet manufacturer from Kidderminster, took over Much Cowarne Rectory in the early 1950s as a warehouse for hop requisites. Hop growers of course have a use for shoddy, the waste from the carpet factory, as a bulky organic fertilizer.

An essential part of a hop sundries supplier's equipment is the balling machine, used for winding into balls the coir yarn made from coconut fibre imported from India. With exotic names like Anjengo or Alapat according to the part of the continent where it originates, this arrives in England, in bales, in the winter months to be balled by local women. Some local growers, such as Neston Capper from Lower Hope, Ullingswick, until he retired in 1984, also had their own balling machines enabling them to find useful work for their own staff during the quieter period of the year. When balled the yarn is taken to the farms to be strung between the ground pegs and the hooks on the top wires forming a trellis for the hops to climb. The tool used for this operation is a 'monkey', a long rod with a tube attached to the side of the one end through which the string from a bag carried by the 'stringer' is threaded and guided from peg to hook. It is a very skilled job to get the string to run quickly and smoothly without cutting through your hand in a few minutes, and a badly wound ball can be frustrating to a novice to the point of dementia if it keeps jamming. Artificial yarns have been developed from polypropylene which are much easier to manipulate with speed. Unfortunately this material degrades in sunlight and when first used on its own a great number of bines fell to the ground later in the season.

Winding hop string in Pettifer's workroom at 7 High Street, Bromyard, as it was until the 1960s.

Balling Machine. The ready spun and plied (2 ply) coir came from India in compressed bales (about 3 cwt each), suitably wrapped and strengthened with canes, which were hoisted from the carts in Little Hereford Street to the workroom on the top floor. Once unwrapped the ready made hanks of string were unravelled from the bale and placed over the 'dolly', a revolving cone standing about 4 feet high at the side of the balling machine. The end of the string was fed through the hollow shaft, round the pulleys on the 'flyer' and tied to the spindle of the headstock. When the spindle and the flyer were rotating the string was wound into a ball, or rather cheese shape, by moving the angle of the spindle with a handle attached to the movable headstock. Pettifers marketed the hop string under the trade name 'Samson'.

Erecting a new hopyard at Upper Lyde in the severe winter of 1962-63. Norman Watkins (on the ladder) and Frank Price fixing the anchor wire to a post.

Erecting the framework at the end of a hop row. Tom Wheale and a casual worker.

One of the essential elements in hop processing is the need for fuel for their drying, and early kilns were heated by charcoal or hardwood, and later coal. A particularly suitable coal was obtainable from the south-west flanks of the Wyre Forest coalfield in the Worcester/Shropshire borderlands. Here, outcrops of two series of coal measures occur: (i) the 'Productive Coal Measures', and (ii) the 'Upper Coal Measure' – also known as 'sweet' and 'sulphur' coal respectively. These sulphuric upper coal measures were extensively mined in the west and south of the coalfield at such pits as Bayton, Mamble, Hollins and Pensax. This fuel gave off sulphur when burned and was favoured for hop drying as it improved the colour of the hops. Not far away, the Darby family discovered the process of converting coal into a form of coke in the early 18th century; there is a record that in 1717 'chard coal' was to be delivered annually to the vicar of Lindridge some twelve miles north of Bromyard, and it was probably in use locally soon afterwards. Through the 19th century and until just before the First World War, hop growers in the Bromyard district hauled bulky loads of coke (known as charks) from Pensax and Mamble for their kilns. With teams of horses and wagons the return journey of up to 60 miles took two days across quite challenging terrain and was accomplished with much relief and refreshment. Even today (1988), fifteen years after the closure of the last pit, there is still evidence of the mine-workings. With the coming of the railways, another smokeless fuel, anthracite, had become available from South Wales, and by 1900 this was also fuelling steam engines used to drive fans which forced air through the kilns. (See Chapter 12 for more recent developments in hop drying.)

George Wargent of Ledbury, who published his recollections in 1905, remembered coke being hauled from the Forest of Dean at hop picking time. A huge wagon with side boards, drawn by four horses, would depart one day and return the next. He also recalled droves of donkeys bringing fuel from the Forest, each carrying two bags of coal or coke.

FETCHING THE CHARKS

Nowadays, with oil delivered by road tanker, fuel is no longer the problem that it used to be when charks had to be hauled by the farmer from a colliery. In 1908, the 'boy' accompanying the last wagon loads of charks hauled from Mamble Colliery to Gold Hill Farm, Bosbury, was Inett Homes's father, and Inett compiled the following account of the journey from the description his father gave him fifty years before:

'In the local hop growers calendar one of the major events was fetching the charks, used to dry the hops, from the colliery at Pensax. Two wagons and ten or twelve horses could only just make the twenty mile journey from Bosbury to Mamble and back in two days. Two wagons with eight horses could make the journey but it took longer, as on the many steep hills two trace horses had to be taken back down the hill to help the second wagon up. The charks were very light and so that the wagons could haul a large load of four tons or more, what were known as chark boards were put on the top of the wagon to raise the sides 4 to 5 feet. They were built like the

Wrapping the No.6 wire (to which the string will be hooked) to the 'roping' wire at the end of the hopyard. Upper Lyde.

Wireworking gang fitting No.6 wires.

A wireworker using stilts to put up wire in a new hopyard at Frogend, Castle Frome, about 1980.

sides of a boat and curved outwards so that the accommodation was larger at the top than at the bottom. In some places they were known as charky boards, but certainly round the Bosbury area they were called chark boards.

Prior to the event, wagons and chark boards were overhauled and checked for any damage, axles greased, lamps provided, harness cleaned and checked, and brasses polished. The horses would be in first-class condition and shod with new shoes all round, and a spare set carried in the tool box. In the wagons were placed a cask of cider for the colliery manager, two casks for the colliers, a ham for the manager and a side of bacon for the colliers. Without these it was not possible to get the wagons loaded on the first evening. Also in the wagons were two days' food for the horses, and two days' food and drink for the wagoners and carters.

As these wagons carried food and drink it was common for them to be waylaid and robbed on the journey. For this reason the 'boy' was put in the wagon and given an iron bar with instructions to hit any hands or heads that came in sight over the top.

On the morning of departure, the horses were cleaned, watered and fed long before dawn, and everyone adjourned to the kitchen for a huge breakfast. At the crack of dawn the convoy set off on the long, hard journey, stopping at intervals to water the horses, and at the Baiting House, Upper Sapey, for bait or elevenses. With luck they arrived at the colliery by the late afternoon and were loaded up that evening.

On the High Lane there were two ambushes and, but for the help of his dog in the wagon with him, Father thought they would have been overpowered and robbed.

The night was spent under the wagons and at dawn next morning they started back home, on the harder and more dangerous part of the journey. These wagons, which when loaded weighed nearly four tons, were equipped with double shafts so that there were two shaft horses side by side and four trace horses in front. There were no brakes and the two shaft horses had to hold the wagon back on hills. On steep hills a heavy cast-iron slipper was placed under one rear wheel and the wheel tied. It then slid along the road on the slipper. At the bottom of the hill the slipper would be too hot to handle but it had to be picked up and hung on the hook provided. To prevent the wagons running backwards if stopped on a hill, a wood and metal bowler trailed along behind a wheel and on a jerk of its chain would squat the wheel.

The journey home was uneventful except for a gang of wives complaining that their husbands were off work because of injuries received in fights. A few coins and a lump of bacon were thrown on the road and the women started fighting amongst themselves as to who was going to get the biggest piece.

At Bishops Frome the wagons were met by someone who galloped off home with the news that they were safely down Summerpool Hill. They arrived at Gold Hill at dusk, tired but happy that they were safely back. The horses were watered and fed and everyone entered the kitchen for a huge supper. If, as was often the case, it was a joint expedition between two or more growers, one usually provided the departure breakfast and the other the arrival supper.'

Building a new Kiln at Wick, Pershore, 1910, showing the building trades involved including the foreman.

CHAPTER 11

Twentieth Century Developments in Hop Growing

'Considerable quantities of hops are grown in Herefordshire; especially about Bromyard; – in that part of the county bordering on what may be called the Hop District of Worcestershire.'

William Marshall, 1745-1818.

(This Chapter and Chapters 12 and 14 have been contributed by Harry Paske.)

Few industries have changed more than hop growing in the last seventy years. The fundamental part, the hop has changed; cultivation, pest, disease and weed control, picking, drying and marketing have altered, and the growers and their labour have had to develop entirely different skills.

Scientific research has played a great part. This used to take place only at Wye College and East Malling Research Station, both starting in Kent in the latter half of the 19th century. In 1949 the Ministry of Agriculture & Fisheries (later: Agriculture, Fisheries and Food; MAFF) bought the 176 hectare Rosemaund Farm only eight miles south-west of Bromyard and developed it into an experimental husbandry farm, the only MAF establishment growing hops. The 16 hectares of hops already there were progressively grubbed and new hops planted on fresh ground. In January 1959 the first *Report on the Experimental Work on Hops* by E. L. Jones, the farm director, and N. Moss, the hops manager, appeared. This imparted information discovered about subjects such as cultivations, manuring, dressing and training, and observations on 'New Varieties', all of which were of immediate concern to growers, particularly those farming under similar conditions in the Bromyard area.

The big chemical firms also played a part: in the 1930s ICI did experiments at Dormington Court, near Hereford, showing that hops could be grown satisfactorily with artificial fertilizers in the total absence of organic manures, and since the war the big companies have continuously developed chemicals for pest, disease, and weed control, many of which have been tested at Rosemaund prior to and concurrently with farm use. Since the 1950s scientists and specialists from the Government advisory services must have visited all the hop farms in the Bromyard area, giving profitable advice based on Rosemaund trials, to growers with problems.

It is well known that it is easier to get into difficulties with hops than with any other crop on this planet and a plot of hops is certainly no bed of roses. Rosemaund ceased doing experimental work on hops in 1998, although MAFFs successor DEFRA (Dept. for Environment, Food & Rural Affairs) continued to sponsor research at

East Malling & the Wye College Hop Department until 2006. The National Hop Association of England now sponsors and coordinates hop research.

Hop Varieties

Pressures of economics and plant health have imposed the adoption of new varieties, and Dr Ray Neve, O.B.E., who retired in 1984 from managing the breeding programme of Wye College, was so successful that brewers found difficulty in testing his 'offspring' quickly enough to develop the processes required to use them.

The objective of breeding is to combine genes responsible for alpha acid (which determines the bitterness and preservative value), aroma, high yield, specific disease and pest resistance, vigour (subject to suitability for modern machine picking), and tolerance of difficult conditions and any agricultural malpractice the grower can manage.

It is amazing that, in spite of the tremendous popularity of new varieties with growers and brewers, the aroma hops, Golding and Fuggle (introduced in the late 18th and 19th centuries respectively), have held their popularity. In 1988 they occupied 20% of the total area, and by 2003 this had risen to 32% mainly due the faster decline in the other varieties. They have been re-selected several times, but are all descended from the original stock. Fuggles, a coarser hop than Goldings, are able to tolerate the cold, sticky Bromyard soils rather better, but are less valuable. Some yards of these varieties, for instance at Burlton Court when farmed by the late Phil Hodell and at Nunnington when farmed by Mr Garlick, are known to have been grown continuously for a century. However, the Fuggle variety is struggling to survive due to its susceptibility to wilt: between 1950-70 the area planted with Fuggles decreased by 60%. In the course of gapping up dead stocks, some yards have gradually changed over from one variety to another. I suspect that the present laws relating to description of goods would often have been contravened. The story is quite true about the Bromyard farmer who, while walking his growing crop was asked by his hop factor which yard the Goldings were in, replied 'Well, I haven't really made up my mind yet for this year.' Variety confusion has also occurred on an international scale. Yugoslavia used to obtain Fuggle and Golding plants from England after the First World War, selling the resulting crops to British hop merchants. When the fungus disease, downy mildew, appeared in the 1920s, it was fatal to the Goldings in that climate and more Golding roots were imported only to suffer the same fate. The Fuggles, however, were able to effectively withstand the disease and the hops have since been imported into Britain as 'Styrian Goldings'.

The original source of new varieties was North America, the first successful one a seedling discovered in Manitoba in 1916 and named Bullion. It had the advantages of twice the yield of contemporary cultivated hops and a high although variable alpha acid content (bittering property). Extreme vigour and coarse bine made it difficult to pick by hand and when eventually picked mechanically it would often cause damage if the machinery was badly operated. This was not the main disadvantage: it had an exceptionally strong aroma, similar to blackcurrant, which degraded on becoming stale to the characteristic stink known, with comparative euphemism, as 'tom-cat'. Fortunately brewers overcame this. Guinness, who were the main users of Bullion, rid their product of this feline attribute by simply boiling it away.

Through his breeding work at Wye College, Professor Salmon introduced Northern Brewer, a hop of more moderate growth, in 1934 which has the benefit of comparatively high alpha acid (the latest selection of the stock has even higher values because it is bred virus-free) and an aroma similar to that of Goldings. Unfortunately it is rather susceptible to powdery mildew and without modern fungicides would probably never have survived in the Bromyard area. Nevertheless it was a very successful hop. Apart from being popular here it was grown in Belgium, at one time comprising over 65% of that country's total hop area. From there the German hop growers took it up, under the impression that it was a Belgian hop. This misapprehension disturbed the British breeders so much that they added the prefix 'Wye' to the names of varieties produced during the '70s and 'Wye Northdown' and 'Wye Challenger' appeared. These were good yielding hops with, for that time, high alpha acid content and had the additional advantage of resistance to fungus diseases. Unfortunately this resistance broke down after a few years to a more active mutant of powdery mildew so that even these varieties now require protective treatment.

Avant-garde growers like the late Victor Stock of Tarrington tried out a number of new varieties such as Zenith and Omega, all with 'high-alpha' levels. This could be how they 'cut their own throats' because, of course, the more high-alpha hops are produced, the less the brewer needs to make the same quantity of beer. Hops are increasingly being sold purely according to the weight of alpha acid and this means that a hop with a feasible alpha of 10% would earn double the money per acre of one of 5%, which is a good alpha for the old fashioned varieties. Fortunately for the grower of Fuggles and Goldings the remuneration is not yet entirely on so simplistic a basis, for the 'aroma' hops have properties absent in the new varieties.

New varieties in this region must be wilt tolerant – Wye Target, a very high alpha hop, is a popular example. This can withstand the mycelium of the fatal (to other hop varieties) fungus disease, verticillium wilt. This spreads from the root-hairs through the vascular tissues and produces toxins which kill the complete plant including the stock. This highly infectious disease has driven many people out of hop growing in Kent, where it first appeared in 1924. Sporadic outbreaks occurred in Herefordshire after the Second World War but were all extinguished until the outbreak which started in the Lower Frome Valley in 1975 became endemic. 'Wilt' is the AIDS of the hop world and there is no known cure; infected and surrounding plants should be grubbed up, the area fenced off, and grassed down. Very strict hygienic precautions must be taken subsequently. Some farmers consider they have destroyed the disease by going to the trouble and expense of grubbing a complete hopyard for the sake of only one or two infected plants, but others have not been so successful: the disease has cropped up in nearby hopyards afterwards.

By 1988 Wye College was having a certain amount of success in breeding a dwarf variety of hop to alleviate the problems of high wirework and make harvesting a great deal easier, enabling mobile picking machines to operate. At Rosemaund normal varieties have been grown to a height of only six feet with disappointing yields, although valuable technical information has been obtained. The subsequent development of the Dwarf Hop Story can be followed in Chapter 13

Cultivations

The old system of earthing up the hops in June, in order to smother the weeds and prevent further basal growth, required the removal of the soil in early spring the next year so that the ground pegs for the string could be set right, and the old bine cut back to the crown of the plant to prevent stocks becoming too big and having shoots grow up all over the hopyard. At Little Froome the practice was to plough two furrows width away from the hops with a standard Fordson tractor and Ransomes hop plough, finishing off the job by ploughing as close as possible to the roots with an old Kell swing plough which was designed for horses but used behind a tractor with a drawbar adaptation. A walking man still controlled the plough from behind and would soon become the most unpopular person on the farm if he left too much soil to be stocked away by the following gang. Stocking away the soil to clear the hops which one then

Before the modern 'No Cultivation' system the first spring cultivation was ploughing the soil away from the hops. This was a hydraulic David Brown plough adapted by the Bruff company. T. Wheale driving.

If conditions were not good enough for the 3-furrow plough to do a good job, a swing plough – here a Kell – was controlled by the ploughman to leave as narrow a slice as possible. T. Wheale on the plough.

An alternative tool for removing the ridge was the kerf, or stocker, here framed by the cranked cutting hook stuck into the pole in readiness for the next operation. Norah Wheale at Upper Lyde.

cut back to the crown with a cranked hook, known as 'throwing down and cutting', was one of the hardest jobs I have ever done. To add insult to injury I used to work alongside Jim Walton, an eighty-year-old countryman who was by then half blind. 'Alongside' is the wrong word; he did the job literally twice as fast as I could and I never saw him sweat or heard him grunt. But he did spit on his hands.

It was no wonder that attempts were made to alleviate this hard labour! The Bruff Company of Suckley and Ted Wargent of Canon Frome eventually developed machines which were operated from the power-take-off points of tractors and flailed the soil from the hop rows with rotating arms. These machines had to straddle the hop rows in order to work and so were made with ingenious mechanisms to move them out of the way when they came to a pole.

The system still suffered from the disadvantage of having tractors on the ground at a time of year when soil was often wet enough to be compacted. Compaction restricts root growth and is nowadays ameliorated by implements which are drawn through the ground to shatter the compressed layers when conditions are dry enough in autumn. It is preferable but almost impossible not to cause the compaction in the first place and Rosemaund EHF experimented with the idea of not ploughing hops at all, but grassing them down and keeping the grass short, so that compaction damage in the wetter months could be kept to a minimum. This system was hardly ever used outside the experimental farm because grass robbed the hops of nitrogen and had to be continuously mown during the summer with gang mowers.

Since then the practice of 'non-cultivation' has been developed in which the ground is kept clear of weeds by spraying with simazine and paraquat. Simazine is a pre-emergence weed killer which kills seedlings at germination and paraquat kills any green growth that it touches. With the recently developed systemic herbicides which can kill creeping grasses without harming hops there is now no need to cultivate hops with implements at all, except to incorporate farmyard manure, and many farmers such as Charles Pudge of the Frogend, Castle Frome, do manage their yards in this way.

Environmentalists need not worry about the use of herbicides. Cowslips grew and flowered among my hops where under the traditional system they were absent. I soon realised that the acidity of the yard had deteriorated to pH 5.5! Needless to say they don't grow there any more!

This Bruff 'throwing down' machine used rotating tines to throw the soil from the hops, leaving very little to be removed by hand tools. Upper Lyde.

It is still advisable to cut back the old remaining bine to ground level each year because of the risk of it harbouring pests and disease. The back-bending necessary with the use of a cranked cutting hook for this job is avoided by some growers by using a small, motorised rotary cutter hung from a harness on the operator.

Manuring

Most growers use an organic fertilizer such as farmyard manure or slurry as a basal fertilizer and it is generally considered to be advantageous to the humus content and thus the structure of the soil. This has not actually been proven under the conditions of modern non-cultivation methods and it may no longer be necessary. Some of the fertilizer firms have developed pelleted semi-organic fertilizer which they claim to be better than pure, so called, artificial manures because of the more gradual release of some of the nutrients. I am not convinced that this slight advantage justifies the extra expense of these fertilizers. In fact I have not used any kind of organic fertilizer on hops for several years. Time was available for application during the winter months and damage by tractors and muck-spreaders to wet soil (particularly on the Bromyard soil series), was much more than any benefit accruing from using fertilizer in organic form. Neither do I believe that dung from a pedigree Hereford bull worth £30,000

The final operation, where the shoots were cut back to the crown of the plant. The handle of the cutting hook was cranked so that the worker's hand kept clear of the ground. Tom Wheale at Upper Lyde.

is any more use than that from a store bullock worth £300. However, if the muck is available, cheap, and conditions are right, FYM is quite a useful crop nutrient although the chemical contents can only be estimated.

ADAS (Agricultural Development and Advisory Service) or fertilizer agents will analyse the soil and inform the farmer of its status of phosphate, potassium and magnesium on an index of 0-6 and lime according to pH value. Hopyard soil samples are taken at two depths below the surface, 0-6 inches and 6-12 inches. These give an indication of how quickly the nutrients move down through the soil and requirements for future years. Starting a new hopyard on a fresh site it would not be impossible to have indices of 0. In this case applications of perhaps 280 lbs per acre of phosphate as P_2O_5 and 400 lbs per acre of potash as K_2O may be necessary. According to conditions, the phosphate index with this type of application could very well build up to 3 after a few years when only 200 lbs per year would need to be applied. Potash would not build up so fast but it would certainly increase in Bromyard soils so that much less would be needed with regular application. A rare possibility that may occur in a very dry season is magnesium deficiency, promoted by excess potassium and giving the leaves a very pretty bright yellow edge. Epsom salts is the answer to this.

Hops have always been considered reasonably tolerant to acidity down to pH 6.0, but recently, using BDH indicator, much lower pH has been found in patches of hops in a yard, subsequently the hops failing completely because of particularly localised lime shortage. A soil sample properly taken gives only an average of the yard's condition, so nowadays a pH of 6.0 most likely requires immediate treatment, because some areas would be less.

There is no point in analysing soil for nitrogen as its availability varies so much throughout the year and nitrates are so easily leached away in winter. Work done at Wye College in the '30s and '40s indicated an optimum response at 270 lbs of nitrogen per acre and at one time I used to follow that practice. Unfortunately twenty years ago it was difficult to drive fertilizer spreaders so accurately as today and great dollops of nitrogen fertilizer used to be dropped in the end ten yards of the rows as the tractor drove slower on entering and leaving. Consequently growth became so 'housey' that nests of the pigeons that took advantage of the leaves were sometimes invisible until the bines were pulled at hop picking. Nowadays, with research at Rosemaund having been taken into consideration, nitrogen recommendations have been decreased, and if wilt is a danger, no more than 170 lbs per acre should be used. Some growers manage with even less but their soils probably have a higher humus content.

Pests, Diseases and Problems

Growers in the Bromyard area were introduced to modern pest and disease control and equipment by Pest Control Ltd., the contractors who took over the army searchlight post just out of town on the Hereford road after the war. In the past aphids have probably been responsible for more damage to growing hops than any other agent, and before reasonable control measures were available in the late 19th century they often had a devastating effect. Ladybirds and their larvae were known to destroy this pest and swallows, also, had often been observed destroying quantities of the winged form as they left the hopyards for their winter quarters on plum, damson and blackthorn. Although this would have been a satisfying sight to a grower the fact that this activity was evident at all meant that sufficient fly had been breeding to have already done considerable damage to the crop. Unfortunately, according to the Board of Agriculture's leaflet no. 55, *The Swallow*, published in 1904, swallows had become so reduced in numbers that their influence in keeping down hop flies was very much less effective than formerly. But, to quote the leaflet: 'It is said by some observers that the regular recurrence of hop aphis attack known as "blight" year after year and their alarmingly increasing intensity are due to the absence of swallows. This increase is, however, more probably due to the plan of planting prunes (sic) in the alley.'

During and up to the end of the Second World War aphids had been mainly controlled by nicotine powder blown by a dusting machine. The operation needed doing in still air so that the dust would hang in the hops and because the job was so urgent was often done overnight, the men carrying on with haymaking in the daytime. Similarly very fine sulphur dust would be applied for mould, and Bordeaux powder as a preventative for downy mildew.

An early Drake and Fletcher hop-powdering machine driven by Ned Watkins. Note the hurricane lamp for night work.

It was a relief to be able to delegate the job to a contractor, particularly as the new chemical sprays developed from war gases were so effective. One could walk down the hop row behind the sprayer, being covered by the aphids as sudden death made them relinquish their grip on the leaves. By natural selection aphids gradually acquired resistance and even immunity to the original aphicides, new ones having to be continually developed. Pest control has now became a race against the pest's ability to adapt against chemicals.

Since the Second World War we have been fortunate to have had two products which when applied to the roots and absorbed into the sap killed any aphid that sucked. The first one, used originally in the early 1950s was named Terra Sytam by the makers – 'Terra' because it was applied to the soil at the base of the bines, and 'Sytam', an acronym for 'Save Your Time and Mine', which it certainly did in the early days because no subsequent aphid treatment would be required. It was unfortunately necessary to wear a gas mask when handling the concentrated material because a good sniff when pouring it into the spray tank could be fatal. There were several occasions when people had alarming experiences from slight splashes onto the face. This chemical became gradually outdated and its replacement, cytrolane, was even more efficient. Problems with aphids occur only in very dry years when sap movement is sluggish. Cytrolane is no longer made and has been replaced by even safer, although no more effective products.

Red spider mite can probably destroy hops quicker than anything else. Fortunately it only occurs in very hot weather, but it is so small that most people cannot see it with the naked eye. If infestation is suspected because of the peculiar brown tinge of the leaves, a useful test is to spread fine dust onto the underside of the leaf. This makes apparent the fine web spun by the creature. Immediate treatment with a modern chemical is essential but effective, so long as it is not a spray to which the mite is becoming immune.

Fungal diseases also acquire resistance. Ridomil, a systemic chemical against downy mildew, had previously been effective against potato blight but the disease had developed resistance after only two years of commercial use. The makers then (1988) decided to sell Ridomil only as a mix with copper, the active ingredient of the old Bordeaux mixture, and this new two-pronged attack, the Ridomil acting systemically in the sap of the plant and the copper preventing external infection, was successful on hops. ADAS ran a downy mildew warning scheme which notified growers of specific downy mildew danger periods. Unfortunately some years just seem to be a continuous danger period so we have to use a downy mildew prophylactic every time we spray.

The practice of stripping the lower three or four feet of the bine of leaves is a protection from powdery mildew because it prevents spores leaf-hopping from the ground to the upper parts of the plant. This used to be done by hand but is now carried out with defoliant sprays. As the sprayer cannot be selective, weak hops are protected by transparent polythene sleeves during the whole season.

Most farmers spray their own hops now. Several factors have caused this: hay-making is not such hard work as it was; expert advice is available from MAFF and commercial advisers; hops need treatment more often; and there is the very great danger of rampant verticillium wilt infection being transferred by tractors and machines travelling from farm to farm.

In order to prevent unnecessary treatment and to make necessary treatment more timely and effective, pest and disease warning systems have been developed. Rosemaund EHF has a weather station which collects data relevant to the spread of disease and pests – humidity, temperature, rainfall, etc, as well as a spore trap by which diseases moving through the atmosphere can be identified. There are several other such sites on hop farms in the area and the information can be used to save the grower a lot of money. The most astoundingly accurate service is the forecast of the fly-in of the aphid from the damson and blackthorn trees in the first half of June. During the last few years, the forecasts, made a month previously, have been accurate to within twenty-four hours. Unfortunately, in 1986 the forecast was ten days early.

In certain seasons, hops have a tendency to produce leaves from between the petals of the cone itself, and the varieties which are particularly prone to this aberration, Northern Brewer and Northdown, can be downgraded in valuation if affected hops are present. It has been discovered that production of these 'cock' hops can be prevented by spraying a natural plant hormone, gibberellic acid, specifically when the plant is producing its fifteenth node, usually at a height of about 5′6″ during the third week in May. It may be necessary to spray twice with a few days interval in order to catch the maximum number of bines at the right stage. This treatment delays the production of the 'burr' by about a week, consequently producing more. The resultant hops tend to be smaller but the actual weight produced is heavier, more often than not.

Virus disease is perhaps the most complex problem of all. Sufficient information has been obtained during the latter part of the 20th century to facilitate effective control, but for some time scientists could only infer the existence of some of the viruses. Nettlehead, which mainly attacks Fuggles, is visually the most obvious disease and is probably caused by a combination of three different viruses. The effect is a general weakening of growth early in the season which later causes the growing tips, unable to climb, to fall back from the string. The leaves develop a similarity to nettle leaves only producing one tip instead of three lobes. In some seasons growth will improve in good growing weather but the plant declines over the years, although rarely dying out completely. In the past this fact has encouraged growers to continue producing hops from infected yards which were becoming increasingly worse and losing a lot of money.

Mosaic, a disease of which Fuggles is a symptomless carrier but which drastically affects Goldings, is a completely different matter. This may kill the plant in one or two years and in badly infected areas it may be difficult to keep a hopyard in existence for ten years, especially if the Goldings are grown close to Fuggles or other carrier varieties.

Virus disease also considerably decreases the alpha acid content, a serious economic loss with the new varieties. In the 1960s East Malling Research Station in Kent discovered that one of the main culprits, the arabis mosaic virus [AMV], was transmitted through the soil in the body of an eelworm, the 'dagger' nematode, a threadlike creature about a millimetre long. Rosemaund EHF later collaborated in trials, fumigating soil in an infected hopyard with a cultivating tool that injected a sterilant into the ground and counting the eelworms present before and after. These trials were combined and compared with varying periods of fallowing the hop ground. Without fumigation a fallow period of two years was necessary to destroy the nematodes but a fallow period of only one year was necessary if the soil was sterilised, a considerable economic saving. The toxicity of the chemicals used made soil sterilisation a very specialised job and it is now no longer practised.

Peter Davies of Claston, in the Lower Frome Valley, who had a serious nettlehead problem in most of his hopyards, was also collaborating with Mike Thresh and his team of scientists from East Malling and by 1970 was confident enough of the trial results to plan a grubbing, fumigating and fallowing system in order to change over to new varieties. By 1976 he had been so successful that only ten infected plants could be found in his seventy acres of hops.

The buds on hop setts are a delicacy greatly appreciated by slugs and if there are too many to share in the feast they can cause substantial losses in a young crop. Proponents of organic farming methods will probably say that slug damage is inevitable, as slugs are also found on rotting materials, and if they are deprived will make the most of what food is available. But methiocarb pellets are remarkably effective slug desiccants. Five pounds per acre are all that are necessary even in a corn crop. Slugs rarely recover from contact even in wet weather, and the pellets remain effective in the open for much longer than metaldehyde mixes. Even environmentalists need have no worries: the chemical engineers who developed the poison deliberately made it blue, a colour to which birds are apparently not attracted.

Propagation, Planting and Training

Because it is essential to plant only virus-free stock after the expense of fumigation and fallowing, the traditional system for planting has been superseded. Many farms used to collect the best cuttings resulting from throwing down in March, plant them in a nursery bed over the summer to develop roots, and lift them in the autumn ready to plant straight into the yard as well-developed setts, the amount of development depending on the weather during the growing period. If the hops from which the cuttings were taken were infected so would be the plants from the setts. Every November the Ledbury auctioneers, C. T. and G. H. Smith used to auction hop roots in the market, until the local verticillium wilt outbreaks made it too dangerous from a plant health point of view. Nowadays, roots are bought from specialist suppliers of stock ['A+ Propagators'], certified free from virus by Ministry of Agriculture inspectors. These suppliers are in areas where hops are not grown commercially for picking: e.g. Norfolk, Suffolk, and Powys.

In order to multiply hops quickly, for instance, if a sudden demand occurs for a new variety, cuttings can be taken from the lateral branches and grown on in pots in a heated mist house. When developed enough these can be planted straight into the yard after a suitable hardening off period, even in the middle of summer. There is very little disturbance to the roots if they are grown in Jiffy pots (compressed peat) which dissolve in the soil so do not need to be removed.

Runners produced by established hops can become a nuisance, producing new plants at every node and in some cases even forming a 'hedge' down the row if the cutting back of the previous year's dead bine has not been tidily executed.

The difficulty occurs at hop tying when selection of the bines for the string can become a problem because the best ones cannot be identified in the conglomeration of shoots.

Rosemaund EHF has developed a way of preventing this by planting setts in polypropylene tubes which are produced by local plastic extrusion firms. Sufficient roots have to protrude below the tubes to be in contact with the soil, but as long as the buds are sheathed they have to shoot upwards, and are thus prevented from producing runners along the surface.

This system simplifies hop tying, and also makes the 'assisted self training' method of growing more effective. Unwanted bines are not ripped out by hand as in traditional tying: workers merely walk through and ensure that each string is furnished with at least three bines (or whatever quantity is required). The surplus basal growth is removed by spraying a defoliant directed downwards. For an, as yet, unexplained reason this system produces lower yields than the traditional way, so very few growers practise it in this area. I use the method myself and will not alter now because so much more labour would be needed posing a much greater chance of contracting verticillium wilt.

Training hops round the string was an arduous kneeling-down job, and the same system is still fairly general but the 'assisted self-training' method practised by some growers can be carried out from the standing position. Mrs. Edwards and Mrs. Hamer at Upper Lyde.

CHAPTER 12

Hop-Picking Machines and Drying

'If hops doo looke brownish, then are ye too slowe,
if longer ye suffer those hops for to growe.
Now sooner ye gather, more profit is found,
if weather be faire and deaw of a ground.'

Thomas Tusser, 1524 ?-1580.

Apart from in America where machines have catered for much bigger farming operations, Bromyard was the original centre of the development of hop-picking machinery throughout the world. In 1934 McConnel Hinds of Martley built a prototype 'flying finger' hop-picking machine. Norman Edwards of Rosemaund (where the Experimental Husbandry Farm is now), having watched the developments, installed a machine for the 1937 harvest. Ernest Griffiths of the Stocks, Suckley, James Bomford of Spring Hill near Pershore, Tom Hawkins at Thinghill Court and Fred Coleman in Kent were also using this early machine. After the war, in 1949, Percy Parker at Newton Farm, Stoke Lacy, also had a McConnel Hinds flying finger machine, although by then it was installed by Rubery Owen of Darlaston. This model, however, never subsequently became popular. George Hinds and McConnel later split up and George Hinds continued with hop-picking machines from Barnard's Green, Malvern. He also designed a Rotobank mobile harvester which could be driven from the PTO (power take off) of a tractor or Landrover and which he exhibited in Germany. Several attempts have been made by different makers to manufacture mobile picking machines but very few have been sold, perhaps because they tend to be too cumbersome for convenient movement in the restrictive wirework of hopyards, and in wet seasons there would be the fear of being bogged down and causing considerable structural damage to the soil.

The most successful hop-picking machines were developed by the Bruff Manufacturing Company Ltd of Suckley. Mr A. E. Brookes, the first managing director, started as a draughtsman for Heenan and Froude of Worcester and also worked as a chemical engineer for a Pershore company. His father-in-law, Mr Bruff, who gave his name to the firm, had been a chemist and developed a fruit tree insecticide which fortuitously turned out to have almost equally effective herbicidal properties, killing fruit trees, and involving him in unfortunate litigation. In 1933 Mr Brookes contracted tuberculosis and had to retire from his work in Pershore. While convalescing he designed a hop-powdering machine and with his father-in-law's help began to manufacture them at Suckley. Mr Bruff died, but Mr Brookes continued designing fruit sprayers, small row crop tractors, hop discs, hop presses and potato planters (potatoes were planted between hop rows).

A McConnel Hinds 'flying finger' hop-picking machine at Spring Hill near Pershore. The man on the left is loading the bines, still wet with dew, while the woman removes the stripped ones.

In 1945 he designed a hop-picking machine and in 1948 he installed the first proto-type Bruff hop-picking machine at Captain Hutton's of Winthill, close to the factory. The next year four 'A' type picking machines were installed at Winthill, Les Bowcott's of Monksbury Court, Tom Bowcott's of Felton Court and Charlie Lewis's of Leighton Court. The machines quickly became in strong demand, orders being executed so speedily that paint was being sprayed on as the lorries were being loaded. Since then the Bruff has exported hop-picking machines to California, Czechoslovakia, Germany, Canada, France, and Poland. Workers from the factory who had never been abroad before travelled all over Europe and to Russia, China and Australia to erect and test the machines and to instruct the local farmers about their maintenance. In 1954, Jack Boseley and Henry Rawle spent six weeks behind the Iron Curtain in Czechoslovakia, supervising the assembly and running of the machine.

In 1962 Mr Brookes designed the 'Mini-Bruff' specially for picking on German farms which only grew a few acres each of hops, and 102 were exported. The German firm Scheibenbogen obtained the licence to manufacture those so Bruff did not export any more there. Bruff became part of the Wolseley-Hughes Group in 1968 and by 1978, sales of hop machinery having stagnated through saturation of the market, it was decided to sell the hop side of the operations to CWF Ltd of Ledbury. This firm served the industry well, obtaining the licence to manufacture a German machine, the Wolf hop bine loader, which won a silver medal at the 1984 Royal Show. CWF has now given up hop-picking machines and Drake and Fletcher of Kent are the main parts supplier.

The use of bine-loaders has done away with the bine loading team of five men in the hopyard. This machine is fitted permanently to the side of a tractor which stays in the hopyard and hitches to the empty trailers returning from the picking machine.

Bruff machine being loaded onto railway wagons at Knightwick Station 1954 (Suckley Station had no crane)   *Suckley Local History Society.*

One of the original A-type Bruff hop-picking machines at Monksbury Court in 1949. The gang in front of the tractor is loading the moving bine track (as in the close-up picture on the left). When the floor is cleared the tractor is moved forward and the draw sheet containing the hop-bines will be pulled off its trailer so that loading can continue. An empty draw sheet can be seen thrown up on to the back of the trailer on the right of the photograph. On the platform about 6 feet above the floor a woman can be seen removing the picked bines from the moving hooks before they come round to be loaded again. The machine was moved in two halves on a special axle and the lane from the shed where it was made had to be widened to get it out; it took three days for the journey from Suckley to Yarkhill. Les Bowcott had little idea of how many workers, tractors and trailers he would need and the first year he employed 48 people, but by 1960 the number was down to 8. So many visitors came to see the machine working in 1949 that over £400 was collected for the Red Cross.

As the tractor drives down the row the loader cuts the bine at the bottom, grips it and releases it at the opportune moment when the tractor has moved forward far enough to pull it from the top wire and deposit it tidily onto the trailer. When fully loaded another tractor takes the trailer to the picking machine. Here operators load the bines onto the bine track, which carries them, inverted, between rotating banks of loop springs which strip them. Any sprays that come off are passed through an automatic spray picker, a moving bed of more loop springs, and the resulting leaves and hops are then passed through a stream of air which sucks out the leaves. There are various ingenious mechanisms for removing bits of strig and everything left passes over inclined, rough surfaced, cascading belts, down which whole hops roll onto the final conveyor for inspection, while any remaining strig and leaf is carried upwards to the waste belt.

The great thing about picking hops by machine is the saving in labour. Unless you have the authority of a field marshal it is impossible to get hundreds of people to do exactly what is required, even if they want to, which is never, and even Montgomery would have been hard put to it in a hopyard. When I bought a machine for 15 acres of hops in 1961 it cut down the picking labour immediately from 100 on the books (which meant over 200 when the families were included) to 14.

Waste from a hop-picking machine.

There were several pressures on farmers to accept machines. The expanding economy meant that wages generally were increasing and it was not so necessary for people to earn money for a few weeks in the year. As has already been explained, the time of the school summer holidays was altered and made it difficult for children to be in the yards so the parents could not put in the hours necessary to earn reasonable money. There was always the possibility of a strike by pickers who had a certain advantage because the farmer could never afford to mess about and delay picking.

Wet weather would prevent pickers working. It is not a good thing for the valuation to pick hops in pouring rain, but a day that only started wet could be a complete day wasted with hand pickers. In fact, the quantity of casual labour required made it too unreliable for a modern industry and between 1948 and 1958 the proportion of hops picked by machine rose to 50%; by 1964 the figure was 85% and today all hops are picked by machines.

An advantage of machine picking was that most people who bought a machine were enabled to pick, and therefore grow, more hops than previously, particularly

September 1960 was so wet that hand picking in this hopyard was hindered to such an extent that hops were 'let fly'. Upper Lyde. (The farmer bought a picking machine for 1961!)

if they were willing to upgrade the machine as improvements to increase efficiency were developed. Hop quota became available as some growers gave up, so the average acreage gradually increased and the industry became more efficient still with the benefits of scale. This enabled the bigger growers particularly to keep improving mechanisation and the figures kindly given by Peter Walker of Knightwick show this very clearly (see page 155).

Drying

In the Bromyard area modern developments started in the early 1900s. With an excess of hops being produced more attention had to be paid to the quality of sample. Some seams of anthracite in use for hop drying had been found to contain arsenic and contamination could occur if open fires were mismanaged. This was really a red herring, caused by arsenical poisoning cases in 1900 being traced to beer, although eventually being found due to sugars used in brewing at the time. However, in times of glut, arsenic content was a valid reason for brewers to refuse hops, so this was a factor in the development of oven type dryers which enabled the grower to have 'PURE AIR DRIED' stamped on his pockets. The products of combustion from the fire were led through a number of iron pipes before escaping to the chimneys. These pipes were in the 'plenum' chamber below the hops and warmed the hop-drying air as it moved up through them.

Mr A. F. Partridge, who grew hops at Wharton Court, near Leominster, was responsible for importing a Sirocco dryer from Belfast. Originally designed for tea drying they had very powerful fans and used an 'indirect' firing system, i.e. none of the combustion gases passed through the hops. Neil Parker at Newton Farm, Stoke Lacy, had one of these blowing air through a tunnel which was able to dry three kilns simultaneously, although it was later converted to oil burning with a Jones Rotomiser installation.

Ted Shew, a grower from Cold Green, Bosbury, installed many Shew's Patent ovens made by Jones and Attwood, the manufacturers of greenhouse heating equipment in Stourbridge. The air was forced through the hops by a fan in the bottom of the kiln, unlike the Joyce's Patent where the air was sucked through by a fan in the top. W. Wargent and Sons of Stoke Edith bought Joyce's Patent in 1920, and had a great deal of success after improving the design by enclosing the pipes. In one year they installed thirty. It was reckoned that hops dried by Joyce's Patent won more prizes at exhibitions because the fan above the hops was more efficient at removing the reek from the top layers. Later, automatic underfeed stokers were added, fuel hoppers which fed anthracite to the bottom of the ovens. These were controlled electrically by Oto Control, a development of W. J. Wargent, the senior partner. Oto Control kept a predetermined rate of temperature increase and the same system is in use today, controlling oil burners.

Upgrading of hop-drying facilities in the 20th century, from farm sale particulars.

1911 Leominster Out, Wharton Court, 250 acres, 30 acres hops.

Two brick-built hop kilns fitted with Davidson's Patent "Sirocco" Dryer

1918 Ashperton, Pridewood Farm, 134 acres.

NEW BRICK AND SLATE ERECTION OF FOUR HOP KILNS, each 21 feet square, fitted with "Joyce" Pure Air Drying Plant and two Fans capable of drying three tons per day, also Cooling floor, Bagging Room, Store Room, &c.

1937 Wellington Heath, Jugs Green & Priors Court Farms, 290 acres.

Jugs Green Farm: THE MODERN HOP KILNS … are mostly brick, slated and tiled. They comprise: Four Kilns with Sirocco drying plant arranged in pairs; the first pair each measuring 40 feet by 20 feet with one large and one medium-sized heater, the second pair measuring about 20 feet by 20 feet each with a medium-sized heater.

The Kilns are fitted with Hetherington Patent Roller floors and the hairs have recently been renewed. Adjoining are a 3-bay store room with sliding doors and concrete floor; Bagging room about 83 feet 9 inches by 25 feet with Hoist and Hop Press by Wargent; Curing Room about 40 feet by 20 feet; Cooling Room about 60 feet by 40 feet with Bagging Chamber under and galvanised iron Engine House.

1945 Stretton Grandison, Townsend Farm, 167 acres, 32 acres hops.

A splendid block of MODERN HOP DRYING BUILDINGS, lighted by Electricity and comprising:

2 large Hop Rooms with concrete floors below, 4 kilns (2 of which have 'Redi' Automatic Stokers), 2 'Joyce' Heaters, 2 'Shew' Heaters, 4 fans, Switchboard, Thermometers, Dynamo, 3 long lengths of Shafting with Pulleys, also an extra Fan for cooling Hop Room, an Electric Fan for cooling Hops and 2 Hop Baggers, also a very substantial covered Loading Stage with slatted floor.

A short distance away is BRINSOP BARN: an Enclosed Barn with 3 bays and driving way and concrete floor … also a number of partitions for converting Buildings into Hop Pickers' sleeping quarters.

To be taken at valuation: Hop Wirework… 4 Kiln Hairs (one of which is a rolling hair)… Creosote Tank….

1949 Felton, Rosemaund, 430 acres, 39 acres hops.

Creosoting Tank with fire box under. Four Hop Kilns, No 1 30 feet by 20 feet, Nos 2 and 3 each 12 feet square and No 4 16 feet square. With three No 4 Rotamisor Liquid Fuel Burners complete (installed in 1946) and a 2,500 gallon Oil Storage Tank, Lean-to unloading bays, primary and secondary Hop Rooms and Engine Room with lean-to shed in 2 compartments. Two Bagging Rooms. A "McConnel Hinds" Patent Hop Picking Machine.

The fan from the Sirocco dryer. This fan, driven originally by a portable steam engine and later by a 20 hp electric motor, had sufficient power to dry two kilns 18 feet square and one at 40 feet by 18 feet. The plant was imported from Samuel C. Davidson's Sirocco Works in Belfast in 1911 and dried the hops at Ankerdine until the new kilns were built in 1970.

Cast iron housing for Sirocco fan driven by stationary engine. The casting reads 'Sirocco Patent Propeller Fan Nº 5'. The fan blades have been removed, but the fixing lugs can be seen. *Joan Grundy*

The buildings at Town's End, Stretton Grandison, combined with the 1945 sale particulars, illustrate the constant innovation carried out during the 20th century. In 1889 there were two round kilns, in 1910 there were three kilns, and by 1945 there were four, one with a roller hair. The round kilns were taken down in 1984 and replaced by a two-tier kiln. *Joan Grundy*

Town's End, Stretton Grandison. The top fan and stovepipe of an early 20th century kiln. *Joan Grundy*

Since the Second World War most drying has changed over to gas oil (diesel) fuel with self-contained electrically driven fans, driving the air from under the load.

Farmer Pudge of New House, Bishops Frome, had several of the Urquhart make installed before the war. Since then the most popular has been the Nu-Way, built at Droitwich. This has the advantage of a very high airspeed fan which drives heated air through the hops at speeds of 50 or 60 feet per minute – previously 25 feet per minute was a reasonable airspeed. High airspeeds allow for either deeper loading of hops, or lower temperature drying. The quality is enhanced by drying at temperatures below 140°F.

Hops dried by oil-fired burners cannot generally be classed as pure air dried because the air is drawn directly through the flame to the hops; but as there is total combustion (which is not the case with solid fuel) there is no danger of contamination unless the burner is set incorrectly and pure diesel oil goes through the hops. If this happens the contamination is obvious from the smell. The hops have to be immediately disposed of as waste. Direct air drying has the advantage of fast automatic reaction to changes in the ambient atmosphere. This is essential with the high airspeeds.

The hop kilns at Rosemaund, Felton, built by the Ministry of Agriculture, Fisheries and Food in 1956 to replace four small ridge-vented kilns. There were 35 acres of hops on the farm at that time. Two banks of kilns with greenstages flank the central cooling and pocketing floor. The kilns on the left (each 11 feet square) were designed for experimental purposes; on the right are three larger kilns, each 20 feet square. The fuel tank (below the left-hand greenstage) serves oil-fired burners housed below the cooling floor.   *Joan Grundy*

Safety is another factor much improved by the modern self-contained oil burners. Before electricity was generally available fans were driven by shafts and belts from internal combustion engines or tractor pulleys. It was impossible to guard these shafts adequately and sometimes greensacks would have to be unloaded in the vicinity of rotating shafts, necessary because they provided the drive to another kiln which was already loaded. Indeed, on an external drive a man was once trapped and killed and his body found later still rotating on the shaft.

It has been recognised since the 19th century that the warm air leaving the kiln in an unsaturated state represented an inefficient use of energy. To make use of this waste warm air multi-tiered systems of drying have been introduced. In the simplest two-tier system, as practised in a converted kiln at Richard Bradstock's of Ashperton, hops are first loaded from greensacks onto the top kiln floor, which is made up of perforated plattens which can be tilted open by levers to allow the load to drop through to the lower drying floor. The top floor is again loaded and drying begins, the warm exhaust air from the lower bed being forced up through the plattens to start to dry the upper bed. When the lower bed is dry the hops are removed in carrying bins and the partly dried upper bed is dropped through the plattens and the upper floor reloaded with green hops. The burner can then continue almost immediately at its maximum permitted temperature because there will be very little moisture left to condense in the air from the lower floor, the hops having already been partly dried. Three loads a day are usually done in this manner but if necessary these operations can be carried out continuously with a sufficient supply of hops.

A roller hair kiln at New House, Bishops Frome. The handle being turned by the man on the right caused the roller hair under the hops to roll forward to the kiln outlet and deposit the hops on to the carrying sheet.

Growers such as Peter Walker of Knightwick had four kilns with three tiers to dry 80 acres of hops. The hops are loaded automatically from an elevator into platten-bottomed bins before being moved into the drying area. The second drop releases them into lighter-built bins which are removed and tipped onto the cooling floor by hand. Only three men are needed to operate four of these 20 feet square kilns, working from 7.00 am to 9.00 pm and 55 pockets a day can be managed comfortably. Using greensacks on the old single-tier system nine men were necessary. The first grower in the country to have three-tier drying with completely automatic loading was Mr R. M. Capper of the Stocks, Suckley, saving 40% of drying fuel in the first year.

At Moreton Jeffries, John Cotton had a three-tier Wolf dryer made in Germany and installed by CWF Ltd of Ledbury, who added a fourth tier. The plattens on this loading tier are not perforated so the exhaust air has to be released through the side of the kiln between the two top tiers in order that the operator has a reasonable working atmosphere. John was well aware of the savings in fuel from this system as there was a flow meter in the burner feed. About six gallons per zentner of dried hops is consumed; 5.7 gallons was burnt in the best year, but on the old single-tier system half as much fuel again was used.

The ultimate in three-tier drying was erected at Allied Breweries Ltd hop farm at Brierley Court. Hops were subjected to 'production line' treatment, controlled by pressing buttons. They were first carried on a wire mesh belt over a cold air chamber, originally designed for sulphuring hops. Sulphuring was banned in the year of

		Picking Staff	Kiln Staff
1954	4 Picking Machines + 4 sets of Kilns	☺☺☺☺☺☺☺☺☺☺☺☺☺☺☺☺☺☺ ☺☺☺☺☺☺☺☺☺☺☺☺☺☺☺☺☺☺ ☺☺☺☺☺☺☺☺☺☺☺☺☺☺☺☺☺ ☺☺☺☺☺☺☺☺☺☺☺☺☺☺☺☺☺	☺☺☺☺☺☺ ☺☺☺☺☺☺ ☺☺☺☺☺☺
1968	2 Picking Machines together + 2 sets of Kiln	☺☺☺☺☺☺☺☺☺ ☺☺☺☺☺☺☺☺☺ ☺☺☺☺☺☺☺☺☺ ☺☺☺☺☺	☺☺☺☺ ☺☺☺
1980	2 Picking Machines together + 1 set of Kilns	☺☺☺☺☺☺☺☺☺ ☺☺☺☺☺☺☺☺☺ ☺☺☺☺☺☺☺☺☺	☺☺ ☺
2002	1 Picking Machine + 1 Mobile Harvester & static cleaner + 1 set of kilns	☺☺☺☺☺☺☺☺☺ ☺☺☺☺☺☺☺☺☺ ☺☺☺☺☺	☺☺☺ ☺☺

The effect of improved mechanisation on labour utilisation at Ankerdine Farm.

installation, but the cold air prevents the hops sweating and discolouring, as they are apt to in bulk, particularly if drying is delayed, and there was a bonus in that the moisture driven off by the cold air causes a significant saving of fuel. Hops then pass over the three mesh-belt tiers of the Wolf discontinuous dryer. Although fuelled by oil this is through a heat exchanger so that it is heated by pure air. On leaving the dryer, hops are carried over a 'conditioning' chamber which is only used to apply a little more hot air if the dryer has not done the job precisely enough. From here the next stop is the automatic weigher and baler, and hops are then ready for delivery to the brewery. Two of these units dry 260 acres of hops picked by two Super E Bruff Machines.

Rosemaund EHF and Wye College have played a prominent part in the development of a very cheap method of fuel saving by re-circulation of air. All that is needed is a duct outside the kiln to carry exhaust air from above the hops to the fan heater inlet. This is opened when the exhaust air humidity is beginning to decrease, about halfway through drying, and with judicious operation 15% saving has been achieved. Three farms in the area used this system in 1984.

Hop Processing

Hops still leave the farm in the cylindrical pocket or rectangular bale but a new industry has now been developed between the kilns and the brewery to process them into more convenient forms for the users. Hop Developments Limited took over a local hop farm, Moor Farm at Eardiston in the Teme Valley, and converted it into a factory for refining, powdering and pelleting hops into 'Hopstabil Pellets'. These are vacuum packed and take up much less room than pockets or bales. Pellets can be a blend of different varieties of aroma and alpha hops and produced at a specified alpha percentage at the instructions of the brewer.

Hop Developments Ltd also have at Eardiston a pilot CO_2 (carbon dioxide) extraction plant which uses the most efficient process yet devised to extract the required brewing substances from the hop.

Sulphuring

Before the 1970s, samples displaying a very green coloured bract were very unpopular with buyers, possibly because it indicated immaturity. This was the main reason for sparse nitrogen manuring by some growers. Nowadays the main reason for sparing the nitrogen is the expense, and the greater danger of wilt, for merchants' tastes have changed and green hops are no longer so despised.

It was found that burning roll sulphur under hops at the beginning of drying would bleach out some of the green colour, and Dr. A. H. Burgess, the renowned hop scientist, worked out a formula based on airspeed through the load, ripeness and dampness, for the quantity to be used. Some people would apply a late dusting of powder sulphur to the growing crop not only as a mould eradicant, but in the hope that it would act as a bleach if it became wet. It all seemed a load of codswallop

Some modern drying systems employ bins. These are being pushed into the drying chamber after being loaded with hops ready for the first stage of three-tier drying. Upper Lyde.

After the first stage of drying, plattens are opened in the bottom of the bin to allow the hops to drop through to the tier below for the next stage; three-tier, Upper Lyde.

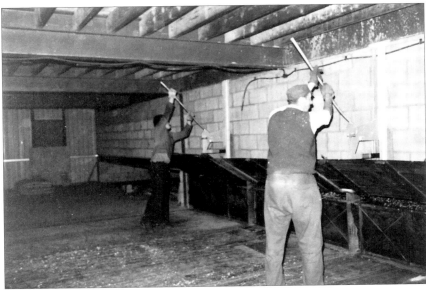

In order to release hops from the second stage to the nylon mesh bins seen behind the open flaps at floor level, handles have to be operated from the cooling floor to open the plattens of the second tier. Upper Lyde.

Hops can be inspected by withdrawing the nylon bins of the bottom tier and returning to the drying chamber if necessary. These bins are light enough to be carried and tipped by two men. Norman Watkins & Tom Wheale.

to me because I could not see any difference in colour between a sulphured and an un-sulphured hop. It paid however because a properly sulphured hop was always valued higher. The late Michael Jackson, a director of the old factoring firm, Selmes, Jackson and Gulland, always held my respect because we used to take samples to him at Worcester Hop Fair and he could grade as many as six differently sulphured samples in order according to the amount of sulphur we had burnt under them, and give advice as to which quantity was the optimum.

Nobody liked using sulphur. It permeated the kilns for half an hour or more after loading and all the grass, and sometimes the farm gardens near the kilns, would be killed by it long before acid rain was ever thought of. The late Les Hinds, the Bromyard builder, who used to help Hubert Baker and Jim Walton in the kilns at Little Froome, told me of an unpleasant experience when the fans in the tops of the kilns were driven by a single cylinder diesel engine. Apparently, this type of machine, towards the end of the week when it had become well and truly hot, could be started merely by turning the flywheel by hand. The kiln had just been loaded and Jim went in to ignite the sulphur with a horseshoe made red hot in the Joyce's oven while the other two went out to start the engine to drive the fan. Unfortunately, when hot, the engine would also run backwards if accidentally started in that direction and that is what happened, without them realising. The fan therefore drove the sulphur back into the kiln resting area, where they found poor old Jim collapsed, and had to drag him out, luckily with no serious harm done.

Oil burners have no stove in which to heat horseshoes so in those kilns methylated spirits was poured into the sulphur pans for ignition. A very tragic event occurred near Ledbury many years ago when a young man accidentally dropped a bottle of methylated spirits in a kiln. It burst on the floor, splashed all over him, ignited and caused burns so serious that he died.

At the Brewing Research Foundation at Nuffield it had been found that the bittering value of hops contaminated with sulphur was reduced, and also that sulphur 'off-tastes' could sometimes be identified in the beer by tasting panels. The brewers asked the Hops Marketing Board to ban the use of sulphur in the kilns in 1980 and, in spite of the fact that valuation had previously been improved, everybody was pleased to be rid of it. In fact, growers no longer dust hops with sulphur against mould after burr because even that can cause contamination.

Cold Pockets

'All Faults' is a subject which is not discussed in the best hop circles because 'it does not exist', and I have found it very difficult to come by any information. Of course I have no personal experience of it. It appears that sometimes hops are not properly dried. The skilled drier removes his hops from the kiln at such a finely judged stage that the slightest maltreatment or carelessness between then and bagging can cause the hops to retain or absorb too much moisture and they will 'perish', exuding a bad, cheesy smell on exposure. They are then useless. If not spotted before entering the warehouse where they are weighed, and samples are drawn, the weight return for the afflicted pocket will be endorsed with the dread initials A.F. for All Faults. Affected pockets can be identified before leaving the kilns by sticking a sharp pocket knife, inclined upwards, into them. If the knife slices through the hops on forcing the handle upwards, the pocket is sound, but if the hops are 'cold' or improperly cured, they are almost impossible to cut. The degree of fault can be ascertained by inserting the probes of a megger and all pockets in the warehouses are so tested. Hop factors visit the kilns during picking, to check on conditions and always carry a megger, but growers themselves are tending to obtain the instruments nowadays.

All kinds of tricks have been tried when cold pockets have been discovered, all of them illegal under the old Hops Marketing Board rules. The simplest was to put the pocket into the plenum chamber at a temperature of 140°F or above, and apparently, with borderline cases, this was successful. A really bad pocket would have to be emptied and re-dried. I believe some driers developed great skill in repacking afterwards so that the treatment was not apparent. The secret was not to press the hops so much in the bottom of the pocket as in the top. Nowadays it is not illegal to treat cold pockets and it is much simpler and easier. Borough Hop Traders Ltd at Thinghill Court have a chamber which freeze-dries complete pockets with no need for any other disturbance.

Modern hop baling. Edward Bonham sewing up bale in a Marsh Bale press at Ankerdine, 1988.

Sampling

Between hop picking and December, rectangular block samples of the dried, compressed hops are cut from the pockets through the side seams, and sent to the factors' showrooms for valuation and display to the merchants. The showrooms used to be in the Borough area of London but have now moved to Paddock Wood in Kent. Originally these used to be illuminated by skylights, but London smog could darken the interiors so much that on some days valuation (which even today depends to a large extent on the brightness and colour of the hop) would be impossible. Eventually, and after much experiment, a special artificial lighting system was introduced, which was also installed in the Paddock Wood showrooms after the move.

Hops were on display not only for merchants: the showrooms were the only opportunity for the grower to see the results of his yearlong labour as a coherent entity, and to study the final effects of his management, which could then be altered or improved as necessary. Thus it became obligatory for all good growers to spend at least one day in London during the winter. Pubs, clubs and shows were ancillary. Factors were, and still are, always extremely hospitable, although in the old unenlightened days when the grower was not supposed to know the merchant who bought his hops, and certainly not the brewer who actually used them, ingenious ploys would occasionally have to be resorted to in order to prevent the meeting of the parties.

Aerial photograph of Ankerdine Farm 1972, showing old and new kilns.

CHAPTER 13

The Dwarf Hop Story

Development of Dwarf Hop Growing

by Peter Glendinning,
Research Agronomist for The National Hop Association of England,
living in Herefordshire.

The labour demands of harvesting hops on tall wirework systems are all too familiar to many of us. Each and every plant has to be cut down and hauled to a static picking machine, so growing hops as a 'combinable crop' has obvious advantages. But the complexities encountered in developing this have been neither obvious nor simple to resolve.

The concept of harvesting hops in the field without cutting the bine is not new, and a number of attempts at it have been made. However, they have all failed, despite the fact that the harvesters developed were largely successful. Such harvesters require plants to be grown as a 'hedge', and there was heavy investment in both wirework trellis systems and new machinery as hundreds of acres were replanted in America and Eastern Europe during the 1980s.

In the rush to realise potentially large savings in harvesting costs, one fundamental factor was overlooked: the yield was appalling! The hop plants were simply not suited to being grown in this way! Traditional hop plants grow naturally 20 to 30 feet tall, and we are all used to seeing them climbing up well-spaced strings suspended from a wirework lattice. The same plants growing as a hedge, in a single vertical plane, tend to produce so much leaf shading that the 'flowers' cannot develop properly into hop cones. Although often overlooked, this has always been known, and is best illustrated by the way the Chinese successfully grow the vigorous American variety Clusters, with its dinner plate leaves, on wirework barely 6 feet off the ground. They snip off enough leaves during the summer months to allow sufficient light into the developing crop, and they achieve yields well in excess of double ours here in England! We could improve our yields in the same way, but we could not hope to afford the six full time workers an acre needed!

An easier and more passive way of avoiding leaf shading is to grow naturally dwarfing plants, and there is nothing new about these either. In 1911, Professor Salmon at Wye described a plant as having 'hops densely clustered, very fruitful, of no direct promise'. It took a visit of UK growers to the hop fields of Washington State (North West USA) in 1976, for Dr. Ray Neve of Wye College and Peter Davies of Dormington to recognise the potential benefit of these 'runt' plants, as described by Salmon, and the idea of introducing this habit into our breeding programme was hatched.

Hop plants at Wye that grew only 8 to 10 feet tall were then selected for further breeding, and in the late 1980s, Dr Peter Darby (who is still the hop breeder at Wye) started to demonstrate their true potential. New varieties were chosen from those with promising yields, high alphas and good aromas; the first being First Gold. All dwarf hops have naturally short internodes and small leaves. They tend to produce short lateral branches with tight bunches of cones, which are of similar size to their taller sisters' – the plants differ only in the length of their bines.

It was largely growers from Hawkbrand and Western Quality Hops that were responsible for pioneering this new crop, which is not only more economic than tall hops, but crucially more controllable. However, a number of agronomic challenges had first to be overcome by detailed field research. This was led by Peter Glendinning, Peter Davies and Edward Thompson, and covered a wide range of topics from improved techniques for plant establishment to self-training, and from pest and disease control to harvesting. The initial obstacle to development was that the practicalities of both growing and harvesting needed to be proven simultaneously; there was no option for growers to invest in one without the other.

Research into trellis systems has shown that the most robust yet cost effective method of supporting the dwarf hop hedge is by suspending a made-to-measure net of extruded plastic on horizontal galvanised wires. These are best held up by poles about 10 metres (30 to 36 feet) apart, and driven 3 feet into the ground. The poles at the row ends lean out into the headland, and are braced to screw anchors or buried sleepers using recycled 'half inch' or 'double nought' wire. Hedgerow hops are much less susceptible to wind tagging, provided that the field boundary hedges are maintained to about 8 feet, so have not stemmed the decline of the traditional hop yard hedge.

A harvester was needed that could pluck the hops from the hedge without bruising or shattering them, and preferably one that was affordable and weighed less than 6 tonnes! The two Johns, Cyster and Eastland from Kent, and Robin Peers from Pattenden Machinery in Herefordshire were the first to put their minds to the task. Pattenden developed a picking and handling mechanism so gentle to the cones that the crop samples immediately started to win prizes. And such was the quality of the sample, that a separate class was quickly created for 'dwarf hops' in the local ploughing matches!

Pattenden's first machine was self-propelled requiring only one driver, and was named after Robin. It was the centrepiece of the MAFF stand at the Royal Show in July 1996, and was instrumental in persuading Government to support hop growers wishing to restructure their hop enterprises. A trailed version of the Robin quickly followed, christened the Wren, and with a lower price tag proved more popular with the growers, despite being slower and needing two men to operate.

The harvesters straddle the 8 feet high hedge, presenting vertical banks of wire finger pluckers to both sides at once. The cones and around half the leaves are picked using much less energy than the static machines, and are caught by conveyor belts made of specially designed interlinked plastic scales. These lift the crop inside the cowling at the rear of the harvester up onto a transverse rubber belt, which discharges into a crop trailer being driven alongside in the adjacent row. This belt can be adjusted in or out to suit row widths, and for driving on the road. It is the size of this belt that limits the speed of field harvesting. The usual forward speed is about half a mile an hour, but when the crop is thin it can be driven faster.

Once safely in the trailer, the crop can be tipped into a dump box or hopper. Originally, it was thought desirable to rid the crop of its leaves in the field, but in fact it is the leaves in the load that prevent the cones from nesting so tightly together that they cannot be easily tipped out after a bumpy ride back to the farm. Even with two Bruff cleaners working at full capacity the Robin will have idle periods in the field waiting for return trailers. The maximum speed of harvesting on most farms is governed either by the kiln capacity or the rollers feeding the spray picker. Some growers have made big improvements by extending the roller beds, since it is the volume of leaves that is often a problem, and the ASP mesh needs to be watched carefully for 'sausages'.

Our hop growers are indeed the world leaders in producing dwarf hops in environmentally friendly hedges. We had anticipated a reduced labour force and benefits from not cutting the bine at harvest giving lower fertiliser requirements, but there have been other pleasant surprises. Traditional hop yards are largely bare from October to April and provide little in the way of cover for wildlife. By contrast, 'hedgerow hops' are seen to harbour a host of wildlife all year round, and are home to large numbers of small mammals and nesting birds. The wide grassed headlands, demanded by the mobile harvesters, are ideal hunting grounds for birds of prey, especially our friend the barn owl.

We have all witnessed a severe reduction in the UK hop acreage in recent years, but the area of hedgerow hops continues to rise, which is not so surprising as 5 out of the last 6 varieties released from Wye have been dwarfs. The most successful variety has been First Gold, which has both a useful alpha acid content and a superb aroma. It is now recognised worldwide, and is even on the privileged list of varieties accepted by Anheuser Busch! But with its alpha acid ranging from 7 to 10% LCV, First Gold is not considered by all brewers to be a direct replacement for traditional aroma. However the most recent variety, Sovereign, is being grown purely for its exceptional aroma, which some leading brewers say is the best 'noble' aroma since Fuggle and Saaz, perhaps even better!

The future of breeding new varieties in England is now in the hands of the National Hop Association, the government having withdrawn funding for Wye in 2007. The programme is being managed by Wye Hops Limited, all the plants having been

A dwarf hopyard, Hilltop Farm, Martley. The posts are 8 feet high.

Comparison of two dwarf varieties, Sovereign and the leafy Herald.
Peter Glendinning

Pattenden Robin picking machine in action. *Peter Glendinning*

Picking machine at Hilltop, Martley, 2006.

moved to Harbledown in Kent under the expert guidance of Tony Redsell, perhaps the industry's most devoted disciple. The work will continue to develop some of the most exciting plant material in the world, which already includes plants completely tolerant of our old adversary, the Damson Hop Aphid!

Table 2. Tall and dwarf hops by variety, 1998 – 2005.

		1998 % of crop	2003 % of crop
Tall hops:	Goldings	20	18
	Fuggles	13	14
	Target	24	13
	Others	34	34
Dwarf hops:	First Gold	7	13
	Others	2	7

	1998	2003	2005
Total tall hops, hectares % of total crop	2217 91	1017 80	817 76
Total dwarf hops, hectares % of total crop	216 9	262 20	254 24

Calculated from National Hop Association data.

The Farming Calendar growing Hedgerow (Dwarf) Hops.

Looking at the year's activities at Hilltop Farm, Martley, the farm of John & Thomas Walker. This enterprise was started from scratch with the first planting in 1995 and without the experience or prejudices of having grown tall hops before.

October: Having finished picking, drying and baling everyone starts the year with a holiday, although there will be sampling being done and possibly the dispatch of bales to the first contracts. If the weather has left the ground still dry enough then sub-soiling is done in alternate rows (with luck in alternate years).

Through the rest of the winter John hopes to see regular dispatches of bales to clear the stock as soon as possible. Cold store or warehouse storage is better than on-farm storage and removes the responsibility from the farm.

In the hop yards there are repairs to the wirework and posts to be done and the replacing of any torn or worn out nets. There is no regular replacing of nets, John tries to get the maximum life out of them. Also the sprayer and other machinery is maintained when the weather is unsuitable for other tasks.

February: Start weed control in the rows before new shoots emerge. This helps the emerging shoots to climb the nets rather than up weed stalks.

April: One of the last winter jobs to be done is sweeping the nets when the bines are dry and brittle to remove as much of the old lateral as possible, otherwise it appears with the crop at harvest and is very difficult to remove from the sample! Great care has to be taken with this task as it is all too easy to catch and rip the net. The one advantage of fitting new nets is that the hops will be free of dead lateral during the harvest of that first year.

By the middle of the month spraying for downy mildew and mould will start as soon as there is a target of new shoots and this will continue as a fortnightly routine for the rest of the summer.

May: Spraying will start against aphids and as soon as it is warm enough predators will be introduced against red spider. Some years these are very successful but cannot be relied upon. There needs to be constant monitoring of all the diseases and pests especially as John reckons that this part of the Teme Valley is a degree or two warmer than further west in Herefordshire and this encourages the earlier development of red spider.

The only 'tying' done on this farm is a walk through when the bines are about 4 feet high (about half way up the nets) to fill any gaps. Some farms spend a lot of money ensuring that only one bine is going up each of the verticals of the net, but John has found this not to be necessary to get a reasonable and consistent yield.

July: Early in the month a compound fertilizer is applied, to 'feed the burr', again some growers go through several times with light dressings of fertilizer but unless there appears to be a problem, John has found a single application works.

August: A nervous time watching the development of the crop until harvesting starts, usually during the last week of the month. Each year since starting to grow dwarf hops John has made some modification to the cleaning machinery which is located next to the kilns at Ankerdine in the attempt to produce a sample free from as much extraneous matter as possible. This has been quite successful as he has won several prizes with his First Gold hops since he started.

Picking, cleaning and drying hops at Townend Farm, Bosbury, 2005

Flow Chart (not to scale)

Both tall and dwarf hops are grown at Townend Farm. The strings and bines of tall hops are cut down together, and taken to the buildings in specially adapted trailers. Here the bines are suspended from the bine track (1) and conveyed through the picking machine (2), which strips the hop cones from the bines. Stray sprigs and broken bines are stripped by the spray picker (3), and the hops are now ready for cleaning.

A mobile picking machine straddles the rows of dwarf hops, stripping the hop cones direct from the bines. In the hop building, the green hops are tipped into a pit (4) and conveyed beneath the picking machines to the cleaning operation.

After passing though a drum where a fan blows off light rubbish (5), the hops pass over a series of inclined belts (6) which carry rubbish to the top, and allow the hops to roll back down to a conveyor which carries them to the two kilns (6 × 6 and 6 × 7·5 metres). The kilns are loaded by a conveyor (7) which travels across the top of the kilns, distributing the hops evenly. Oil and gas burners and fans (8) blow warm air into brick ducts beneath each kiln. The ducts have three branches, each with a spinner on top to distribute the warm air upwards through the green hops.

The larger kiln (9) has a roller hair which draws the dried hops forward into a chute. The second kiln (10) has four tiers. The upper three have floors of tilting slats, allowing partially-dried hops to be successively dropped into a lower tier. The bottom tier comprises two bins. When drying is complete, the full bins are rolled out and the hops dropped into the chute. They now travel to the cooling bin (11) which has a ventilated floor, from where they are drawn off to the baler (12) and packed in stencilled and numbered bales.

Reproduced by courtesy of Mark Andrews, Townend Farm.

170

CHAPTER 14

Marketing Yesterday and Today

'Hops a good deal cultivated, and chiefly disposed of to British dealers.'

John Claudius Louden, 1783-1843.

One of the many problems for hop growers is that there is only one significant buyer – the Brewer, but to try to reduce this dependence, other uses have been explored from time to time.

In Victorian times, for example, hops were used extensively for preserving baking yeast when bread was made from hops, yeast, raisins and flour, and even towards the end of the 20th century a Worcester hop merchant, the late Richard Rayer, had enquiries from Bombay for the same purpose. ISO-compounds derived from alpha acids, which are responsible for much of the bittering and antiseptic power of the hop, are peculiar in that their toxicity is effective against many bacteria, but not against yeasts. Victorian ships all had to carry hops for yeast preservation, and Pike, a London merchant, used to have the Admiralty contract until the early 1950s. From the late 20th century, however, hops find their way on board naval ships only in the beer.

During the First World War, the Germans used hops as an adulteration to eke out tobacco, and before World War II it was quite common to eat the spring shoots like asparagus. Geoffrey Lloyd, the herbal horticulturist from Ocle Pychard, started re-encouraging this culinary cannabic craving in 1984 and was successful in selling shoots to the London restaurants of Harrods and Fortnum and Mason. Other growers have since exploited hops in this way, and when Rosemaund EHF was growing hops, some time was spent studying how best to prepare the shoots. Hops have also recently been used to make ewe's milk cheese more palatable by maturing it for two months in barrels of hops, thereby instilling a uniquely pleasant flavour. It is also possible nowadays to buy Cheddar type cheeses flavoured with hops from any decent cheese shop. Anyone organising a wedding can now become parson popular by insisting that hop petal confetti must be used instead of the paper kind. It is more environmental and doesn't make a mess in the churchyard or hotel foyer to the same extent that coloured paper does, and is treated to prevent the stickiness that would otherwise make it very uncomfortable inside your shirt or petticoat!

Classical writers including Pliny the Elder and Gerard extolled the imagined medical properties of the hop, and even nowadays there is reason to believe in the soporific effect of hop pillows, made by stuffing small cloth bags with a mixture of dried hops, lavender and other preservative. They may be purchased, very reasonably priced, at the Hop Pocket at Bishops Frome. I am surprised that the Health and

Safety Executive has not imposed a rule that intending purchasers should be warned, when using them for the first time, to insert two layers of cloth between the head and the pillow: if one is not used to the ambience of a strong hop aroma one may not wake up at all!

On more solid ground, a compound which apparently is present only in hops, xanthohumol, has been found by researchers at Oregon State University to be one of the more significant compounds for cancer chemoprevention. Most beers contain low levels of it, but I suspect that if enough beer was drunk to be effective, cirrhosis would become a more immediate problem. However, if the United Kingdom public can be persuaded to overcome its abhorrence of genetic engineering it could probably be used to increase the xanthohumol content of hops to more useful levels.

What may be of more immediate value is research being done at the University of Arkansas. Results of the study (published in the *International Journal of Poultry Science*, Vol.5 pp.134-136. 2006) indicated that the addition of ground hops to poultry feed improved early growth rate of broiler chicks and reduced the overall feed needed to produce a pound of live-weight gain. Although the response from the addition of hops was not as great as that obtained from the antibiotic treatment, it was significantly greater than that of birds fed the control diet, and presumably without the risk of inducing antibiotic resistance.

A preservative effect has been observed by Mr. James Edmondson, a member of Lugwardine Historical Society. In 1965 he was visiting the island of Hinnoy, off the coast of Norway. Being obviously an erudite man he was mistaken for a doctor and invited to enter the crypt of a local church where there was an uncomfortably strong smell of formaldehyde which had been used to treat the contents of 29 coffins which had been opened up. There were corpses of both sexes and various ages, probably of the more well-to-do parishioners, who had died between 1760 and 1821. The bodies had originally been eviscerated and embalmed with hops. Admittedly, some had kept better than others, but many of them were in the condition of people who had died only a few days previously. The hops had all kept well! (*English Hops*, March 1988, p.7).

Unfortunately none of these outlets has yet sufficient potential to justify the capital necessary to grow the crop, and even the ones that are presently available can only produce a little pocket money from existing facilities during situations of surplus.

The success of the hop industry therefore depends on the brewing industry.

Four so-called global brewers dominate the industry in the United Kingdom, but fortunately for the discerning beer drinker there are also about 500 microbreweries, 35 family owned breweries and several bigger regional breweries producing an amazing selection of different types and tastes of beer. The government's introduction of Progressive Beer Duty in 2002, allowing brewers producing less than 30,000 barrels a year to pay less tax, has enabled the smaller firms to develop their businesses more during recent years, and it is hoped that not so many will now fold as was previously the case. In Herefordshire and Worcestershire there are presently 16 smaller independent breweries, three of which are, or were originally hop-growers, and use their own products.

At the beginning of the 20th century the UK brewed 37 million barrels of beer per year. By 1918 this had decreased to 19 million, increasing to just over 24 million in 1939 and 31 million in 1945. A peak of 40 million was reached in 1978 decreasing to around the 35 million mark by 2004. During the same period consumption per head decreased from 248 pints (141 litres) in 1900 to 194 pints (110 litres) in 1983; to 174 pints (99 litres) in 2001.

Several factors are responsible for the drop in consumption: the licensing laws introduced with the object of keeping the country working more efficiently during the First World War were never repealed, although they have been amended recently and modern leisure pursuits, the cinema and later television, left people less drinking hours anyway. Mechanisation has abolished much of the heavy manual work in industry and agriculture, and with it the necessity to replace millions of gallons of sweat with millions of gallons of beer. More recently, drinking and driving laws have not helped either, although there are many ways of overcoming the obstacles without being a danger to anyone else. It is too early to say whether allowing pubs to open for 24 hours per day will have any significant effect.

Decreasing the hopping rate, with its stultifying effect on flavour, cannot have done much to improve the popularity of beer. In the 19th century the rate was from 4½ lbs to 6 lbs (2.04 kilograms to 2.72 kilograms) per barrel; because of variation due to different conditions it is difficult to give an accurate figure but it is believed to be about 4 oz (0.11 kilograms) per barrel nowadays. The original factor causing the decrease in hopping rate was a change in taste to lighter beers needing fewer hops; lager uses 40% of that used for bitter beers. In 1969, lager was 6% of beer sales, by 1979 it had increased to 29.3% (Ilbery 1983). Foreign brewers prefer seedless hops, not only hindering English exports but also, as much of the lager brewed in Britain is under licence from foreign breweries, they control the recipe which includes the varieties of hops to be used. Latterly the decrease has been due more to technical advances. Brewers (and merchants) now subject hops to an isomerisation process in which they are treated by immersion in a gas at an uncomfortably warm temperature for a fortnight. This increases the brewing efficiency by 40%. Many of the larger brewers now use hop products rather than whole hops; hop pellets have utilisation levels of 35% to 40% and hop extracts as much as 90%.

The brewers' preference for high-yielding 'alpha' varieties meant that the same amount of alpha acid could be produced from smaller area. Fuggle yields 68.5 kilos alpha acid/ha; Target 171 kilos. A substantial replanting programme was undertaken between 1972 and 1976, encouraged by HMB's incentive scheme, increasing proportion of crop from high alpha varieties from 6% in 1960 to 59% by 1976.

Hop breeders have also played a major part. At Wye College in Kent Professor Salmon at the beginning of the 20th century, followed by Doctor Ray Neve, managed to more than double the alpha acid (the bittering and preservative agent) in hops. Resistance to fungal diseases was also bred into hops but unfortunately the fungi tend to build up an immunity which counters that resistance after a few years. More recently Peter Darby, also working at Wye College, has been responsible for the breeding of new varieties and has miraculously bred an aphid resistant hop named Boadicea as well as continuing the programmes of improvement that he inherited.

Government Interference.

Ever since the days of the Hop Duty (1710-1862) the government has taken a keen interest in hop growing, but in the 20th century this interest mutated into control and interference.

During the First World War a build-up of hop stocks considered sufficient for four years occurred, so in 1917 the Board of Agriculture ordered farmers to cut their acreages to 50% of the 1914 area. A Controller of Hops, Mr G Foster Clarke, was appointed with a committee of four growers, four factors, four merchants, four brewers and four members of the Board of Agriculture to advise. All the surplus hops for the years 1914, 1915, 1916 and 1917 were taken over at valuation and paid for by the government. On Armistice Day growers were immediately allowed to replant up to 75% of the 1914 area but there was a reluctance to do so because of the high cost of wirework.

Importation of hops had to be allowed and then in 1920 the beer tax was increased from 70/- to 100/- per barrel. The effect of this on the hop trade was to convert a severe shortage into a staggering surfeit within the space of twelve months.

The Hop Control body was dissolved in 1925 leaving growers in a difficult position, with a surplus of 100,000 cwts of hops, but the comparative stability under Hop Control gave them confidence to set up a voluntary, elected body of their own, English Hop Growers Ltd. The 'pooling' system was continued, in which all payments for hops were paid into a central pool from which all growers were remunerated. Unfortunately, continuing surpluses and the few growers who stayed outside English Hop Growers Ltd., breaking its power of unity, were sufficient to make things impossible and in 1929 the company was wound up. However the Agricultural Marketing Act of 1931 made it possible for growers to set up a compulsory marketing board in 1932 which every hop grower had to join. The general trading system was altered as little as possible: the hop factors who had previously been the farmers' agents and were responsible for sampling and showing the hops to merchants and brewers, as well as advising growers, became agents to the Hops Marketing Board with much the same responsibility, and merchants continued to select hops on behalf of brewers. This new arrangement saved the situation and was aided in the first two years by a demand in excess of supply.

A letter to a brewery in August 1932 from John Essex Potter of Stanford Court shows his reaction to the Board:

'Dear Sir,

I am writing to ask if you would like to have my growth of hops this year as you have been doing in the past; and to say how much I should like you to do so.

Of course I am compelled to send them to the Hops Marketing Board; but I understand that you will have the option of taking them as in the past. I am told that, under the new arrangement, the factor will sell the hops (as Agents of the Board) direct to Brewers, who can, if they so choose, appoint any merchant, or merchants, to act as their Agents and to advise them, but at the same time the contracts for sale and purchase will be between the Brewers and the Marketing Board.

I have an excellent growth this year again, but Monday's gale has whipped and bruised the hops badly everywhere.

The Factors who will have my hops (with the exception of twenty pockets) will be my old Factors who handled the growth for me previous to my selling the growth direct to you. They are Messrs. Noakes & Banister of 45 Borough High Street, London, S.E.1. The 20 pockets, which I have mentioned, will go to Messrs. Wild Neame & Coy also of Borough High Street, S.E.1.

I think that, in order to make sure that you have the offer of my hops, it may be well for you to write the Marketing Board claiming the first refusal of them.

If you like to come and see the growth before picking I shall be very pleased to meet you Wed or Thursday at W'ster.

Yours faithfully, …'

Quotas were introduced in 1934 to prevent growers selling more than their fair share of hops through the Board in seasons of glut. A basic quota in weight was allotted to each farm, based on previous quantities grown, and, after determining the likely demand from discussions with the Brewers' Society, early each year, the Board would specify the Annual Quota for that season as a percentage of Basic. The percentage could be increased later in the year if the sales position became more optimistic (once it was increased by 6% as late as the middle of hop picking when it became known that the German crop had suffered severely from mould) but growers were only paid the full rate on the weight of the annual quota issued. Unless a grower with surplus was able to obtain extra quota from one with a short crop, his surplus hops, if he picked them, would be consigned to a pool of non-quota account and would probably only receive a small proportion of the quota account valuation.

The monopoly powers of the Hops Marketing Board and the Brewers' Society agreement to accept all English hops on a cost plus basis enabled the Board to control acreage when necessary. The hop price was based on average growing costs plus a percentage profit, and growers were selected at random every year to have different aspects thoroughly 'costed' in order to determine a true average. The costs covered the complete acreage grown whether picked or not, so in a year when hops were 'let fly' because too many were grown, brewers were in effect paying for unpicked goods and put pressure on the Board to reduce the acreage grown. This occurred in 1966. Although beer production was gradually increasing, the hopping rate was decreasing to such an extent that a smaller acreage was necessary.

In the following two years the HMB imposed a levy of £2.14s.0d. per cental (100 lb dried hops) which was used to buy out any growers willing to give up altogether. They were paid up to £900 per ton for their basic quota according to the proportion of annual quota grown in previous years, and altogether 86 producers gave up and grubbed 1,837 acres, a decrease of 11.7 % in two years. This enabled the basic quota of the remainder to be increased by 9.8%.

Beer production continued to increase and English hop acreage to decrease during the '70s due to falling demand for hops occasioned by increased acreage of high

Graph 1. Areas under Hops in the West Midlands and the South East (hectares).

Copyright © H. F. Grundy 2007

Sources: 1835 – Pocock 1959; 1850 & 1900 – Parker 1934; 1861 – BPP1862; 1868 – Simmonds 1877; others – MAFF and DEFRA Agricultural Returns.

alpha varieties. The Hereford and Worcester acreage declined from 6,781 in 1966 to 5,520 in 1976. The figures kindly produced by Peter Walker are typical, and also show that 1976 was the first year he grew only alpha varieties, having grubbed his Fuggles the previous year and Goldings in 1971.

Upon the United Kingdom joining the Common Market in February 1973, there was no longer a quantitative import control of hops from Europe so marketing had to adapt to foreign trading habits to be competitive. This meant the end of the 'cost plus' pricing system and hops had to be offered several years ahead as was already the Continental custom. Previously, if insufficient hops of a variety required by a brewer were available the buyer might agree to accept a substitute, but this was no longer allowed. Thus hops were offered ahead, by variety, at a fixed price. However, the 1976 crop was the first when growers had the unique consolation of an inflation surcharge based on a formula operating from the year of offer.

Falling demand and general world overproduction induced the EEC to impose an order prohibiting expansion of hop area in the Community between 1 July 1977 and 31 December 1979. Although this order was obeyed, even in the Bromyard area, and many hops were also grubbed, the wirework was often left standing and immediately replanted when the order ceased.

When the EEC decreed that the Hops Marketing Board, being a monopoly, was illegal, in 1982 it formed itself into a voluntary body, the Hops Marketing Board Limited and in 1985 became English Hops Limited. Three quarters of the English growers remained as members of English Hops Ltd., the rest forming smaller groups and some even going it alone.

Graph 2. Hop Area 1953-1984 to show changes in varieties grown at Ankerdine.

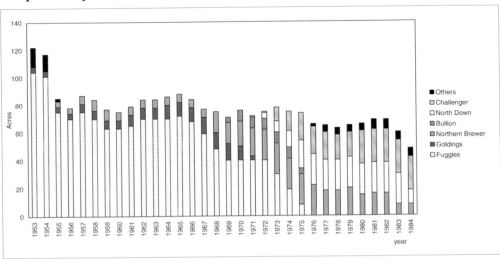

The abolition of the monopoly and compulsory powers of the Hops Marketing Board gave growers freedom to sell how they liked and without reference to the Board, if they so pleased. Pooling could no longer be enforced. This comparative freedom, like the freedom to smoke, could turn out to be a danger to the health of the body and it was essential for discipline to be agreed otherwise there was no point in being a group member. Fortunately, in the case of the English Hops Ltd. this danger was averted after several years of extremely diligent activity by the directors in sounding out the diverse views of the members, and much patient argument and compromise, particularly over pooling. It had become especially important for growers to consider each other as well as themselves, because the total number of growers in England had still declined to less than 320 in 1988.

In 1985 the West Midland area was growing 1787 hectares (4413 acres) of hops when that was 38% of the total, the balance being grown in the South East. By 2005 the area had halved to 837 hectares (2068 acres) and the proportion had increased to 60%. Not that that is any compensation for losing a traditional industry. Between 1955 and 2005 the acreage within a six mile radius of Bromyard had shrunk from 1028 acres to 187 acres, 18% of the original area! According to the June Agricultural Censuses the number of holdings with hops in Hereford and Worcester between 1987 and 2005 had halved from 134 to 66. England in total with only 1402 hectares now has roughly one third of the 1987 area. (See Table 3 below.)

To put these figures in perspective: total world hop area, as far as can be ascertained is probably 80,000 + hectares. The biggest hop growing areas in the world are in Germany, with 17,000 hectares and the USA with 11,912 hectares. (See graph on next page.)

Table 3

FLUCTUATION IN HOP AREAS in HEREFORDSHIRE AND WORCESTERSHIRE
(1995 and 2005 figures supplied by DEFRA).

Year		1987	1990	1992	1995	1997	2000	2002	2005
Hereford & Worcester	Hop Area Ha.	1653	1538	1558	1524	1570	1083	959	837
	No of Holdings with hops	134	116	111	104	98	78	70	66
Herefordshire	Hop Area Ha.			1235	1150	1186	882	805	537
	No of Holdings with hops			87	80	75	63	57	50
Worcestershire	Hop Area Ha.			323	374	384	201	154	300
	No of Holdings with hops			24	24	23	15	13	16
ENGLAND	Hop Area Ha.	4213	3869	3617	3281	3494	2336	1995	1402
	No of Holdings with hops	324	274	248	227	219	178	150	121

Graph 3.

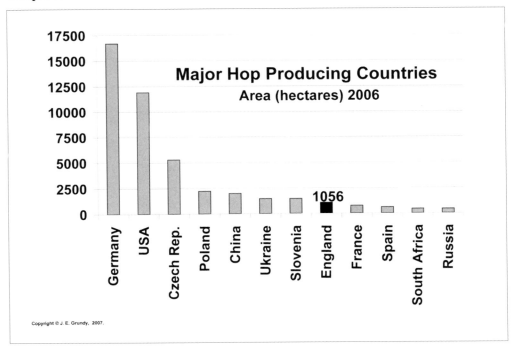

Copyright © J. E. Grundy, 2007.

Source: *Hopfen Rundschau* no 12, 15 Dec 2006.

British brewers have generally preferred to obtain hops from the same farm every year although in many cases, due to the way the factoring and merchanting system worked, the grower himself was unaware of the final destination of his product, except perhaps when a rude letter would arrive from a brewery complaining about foreign bodies, such as pieces of hop-picking machine, being packed with the hops. The brewer had the first chance of the next year's hops off the same farm – this was known as the 'courtesy call'. Some growers objected to sharing the proceeds of their crop with the rest of the 'pool' because, according to their point of view, if their hops were wanted enough to attract the courtesy call year after year they could very well be more valuable than others in the pool and yet they were only receiving the same price – the Customer is Always Right! Of course those growers, if the system was altered, had to be prepared to make a poor sale, or perhaps no sale at all if for some reason their customer changed his mind.

In English Hops Ltd. only one variety, Wye Target, was compulsorily pooled. This was because it was a high alpha hop very suitable for the export market and could be sold mainly on the basis of alpha acid content (i.e. little account to be taken of the brightness or greenness of the sample). Few of this variety were grown in the Bromyard area because they were wilt tolerant and, until a farm was suffering extremely severely from the disease, should not have been grown. For all other varieties growers received the actual price agreed individually with factors or merchants, less of course commission and English Hops Ltd.'s expenses. These expenses covered sampling, grading, warehousing and market information. The company was also responsible for distributing EEC hop subsidies and the collection of payments for research and development which along with a similar donation from the Brewers Society, the Government and other interested agencies, would be used to fund research at Wye College, East Malling, and other establishments. A research and development donation was essential to enable the English hop industry to succeed against extremely keen world competition.

The EEC has certainly made life different for the English grower by forcing the abolition of the HMB although the loss of insularity was to a certain extent at first ameliorated by annual income aid based on acreage and variety of hops. However, so many factors influence the hop trade, weather, disease, new developments in both growing and brewing, labour availability, to mention but a few, that forecasting the future is a mug's game. Who would have thought that our own picking labour force from west of Offa's Dyke would have been replaced by Czechs, Poles, Ukrainians, Lithuanians etc. from east of the Iron Curtain?

In the first edition of this book published in 1986 I wrote appropriately:

But the basic reason for the very real difficulty hop growers are in at the moment is world overproduction which is a problem whether we are in the Common Market or not. It is compounded by the unusually large stocks of hops being held by brewers, a situation due partly to the production of extracts which can be kept much longer than the unprocessed product. Growers hope that supply and demand may be more in equilibrium by 1988 at the latest, but since 1979 British beer production itself has actually been declining – fortunately it is still 150% of 1950 output.

(Beer production was approximately the same in 2004.)

In 2007 there is a global shortage of hops, a situation of no consolation to the many English growers who have been forced out by verticillium wilt, economic conditions or just lack of optimism. Even the old fashioned varieties, Goldings which are 200 years old, and Fuggles, almost 140 years old, are still wanted in limited quantities, but the real optimists are gradually increasing the area of dwarf, or to be politically correct, 'hedgerow' hops which are supposed to have much lower growing costs. This country leads the world in the development of these and the future of hop growing in England may very well depend on them.

During the last twenty years the marketing system has developed further, involving a slimming down process: effectively, hop factors no longer exist, having either given up or been absorbed by merchanting firms. The four remaining small groups of growers sell most of their hops to merchants although EHHL (English Hops and Herbs Ltd. formerly English Hops Ltd.) are selling a greater proportion of hops direct to brewers. Some of the smaller groups still have pooling systems but EHHL does not now pool hops either compulsorily or voluntarily. Furthermore it has an equity stake in Botanix Ltd., the hop processing firm based at Eardiston in the Teme Valley and also at Paddock Wood in Kent.

All these factors, combined with low global prices of alpha acid, increasing costs of production, a market basically limited to UK brewers and the constantly accelerating spread of verticillium wilt, have contributed to the drop in hop acreage in this country. Global over-supply of hops has exacerbated the difficulties, leading to English hop growers, in five out of six recent years, selling hops for less than the cost of production. The United States growers are difficult to compete with, as, apart from their benefits of scale, their growing conditions and varieties enable them to produce much higher yields of alpha acid per hectare than us. The Germans still have a much lower labour cost for aroma hops than us, limiting the amount of aroma hops that can be sold to overseas brewers. However such is the volatility of the market, as indeed with all consumables, that there is now (2007) a global shortage of hops.

Wm. Ed. Le May, Dudley Le May, M.C.,
Stafford Le May, Leslie Le May.

Hop Factors

1872—1949.

RELIABILITY AND SERVICE

W. H. & H. Le MAY

67, BOROUGH HIGH STREET,

LONDON, S.E.1.

('Phone : Hop 1945 & 1946).

Enquiries to Mr. NORMAN H. Le MAY, Hop Pole Hotel, Bromyard (Phone Bromyard 49).

Bromyard News & Record,
8 September 1949.

BIBLIOGRAPHY

Arnold, Richard, *The Customs of London* (1502)

Beale, John, *Herefordshire Orchards – A pattern for all England* (1656)

Berrow's *Worcester Journal* (various years)

Board of Agriculture Leaflet No. 55, *The Swallow* (1904)

Bradley, Richard, *A complete body of husbandry* (1727)

Bromyard Deanery Magazine (various years)

Bromyard News and Record (various years)

Burgess, A. H., *Hops. Botany, Cultivation and Utilisation* (1964)

Clinch, George, *English Hops* (1919)

Defoe, Daniel, *A Tour through the Whole Island of Great Britain* (1724)

Faulkner, Christine, *Hops and Hop-pickers* (nd, c.1990) Faulkner Publications, Brierley Hill, West Midlands

Filmer, Richard, *Hops and hop picking* (1982)

French, R. K., *The History and Virtues of Cyder* (1982)

Gaut, R. C., *A History of Worcestershire Agriculture and Rural Evolution* (1939)

Hereford Journal (various years)

Ilbery, Brian, Harvey's principles reapplied: a case study of the declining West Midlands hop industry, in *Geoforum*, vol.14, pp.111-123 (1983)

Jones, Gwen and Bell, John, *Oasthouses in Sussex and Kent: their history and development* (1992), Chichester

Jones, E. L. and Moss, N., *Report on the Experimental Work on Hops* (1959), Ministry of Agriculture Fisheries and Food, Rosemaund Experimental Farm, Preston Wynne, Herefordshire

Kent, Nathaniel, *Hints to Gentlemen of Landed Property* (1793)

Lance, E. J., *The Hop Farmer* (1838)

Lodge, Rev. John, *Introductory sketches towards a topographical history of the County of Hereford* (1973), Kington

The Leominster Guide (1808)

Loudon, J. C., *Encyclopaedia of Agriculture* (1835)

Lowden, S., *The Locational Change of Hop Farming in Herefordshire* (1981) (unpublished thesis), Aberystwyth University

Parker, Hubert H., *The hop industry* (1934)

Pocock, D. C. D., England's diminishing hop acreage, in *Geography* XLIV, pt.1, Jan 1959, pp.14-21

Robinson, Guy M., *Agricultural change. Geographical studies of British Agriculture* (1988), Edinburgh

Scot, Reynolde, *A Perfite Platforme of a Hop Garden* (1574)

Simmonds, P. L., *Hops: their cultivation, commerce, and uses in various countries* (1877)

Slater's Directory (1859)

Stephens, Henry, *The Book of the Farm* (1877)

Suckley Local History Society, *Aspects of Suckley* (2006)

Tusser, Thomas, *Five Hundred Points of Good Husbandry* (1573)

Walton, Robin and Ivan, *Kentish Oasts 16th – 20th century. Their history, construction and equipment* (1998), Christine Swift, Egerton, Kent

Wargent, George, *Recollections of Ledbury* (1905, reprinted 1998)

Webb, J., *Memorials of the Civil War in Herefordshire* (1879)

The Young Woman's Companion or Female Instructor (c.1800)

MAPS

The Hereford Record Office holds two series (incomplete) of maps useful for tracing old hop yards:

The parish tithe maps and apportionments for the 1830s to '40s

Hop Maps AS78/1-75 (Herefordshire) and AS78/76-124 (Worcestershire for the 1950s to '60s, deposited by English Hops Ltd.

METRIC CONVERSIONS

LENGTH
1 mile = 1.609 km
1 yard = 0.914m
1 foot = 0.305m

WEIGHT
1 ton = 1.016 tonne
1 cwt = 50.802 kg
1 lb = 0.454 kg
1 ztn = 50 kg
110.23 lbs = 1 ztn
1 hop pocket = approx. 80 kgs

LIQUID
1 gallon = 4.546 litres

CURRENCY
1s (shilling) = 5p
1d (penny) = 0.42p
11s 3d sometimes written '11/3' as on p.54.

AREA
1 acre = 0.405 ha.
1 hectare = 10,000 sq.m or 2.471 acres

Hop acre: see glossary

At a planting of 4 feet by 8 feet (1361 plants per statute acre)
1 hop acre = 0.73 of a statute acre

At a planting of 3 feet by 8 feet (1815 plants per statute acre)
1 hop acre = 0.55 of a statute acre

GLOSSARY

acaricide	chemical used to kill red spider mites
alecost	costmary *(Chrysanthemum balsamita tanacetoides)*
alehoof	ground ivy *(Glechoma hederacea)*
Anheuser-Busch	large brewing company based in USA
aphids	sap-sucking insect pest which are the vectors of plant virus diseases
ASP	automatic spray picker
bagging hole	see treading hole
bait	food for break time
barrage balloon	large tethered balloon to deter low-flying aircraft
beethy	uncrisp, leathery
bin	Kentish term for large, round picking basket, and later for a crib
bine	twining stalk or the whole top growth of the hop
bittering rate,value	see hopping rate
Black Country	heavily industrialised region of the West Midlands
blight	see aphids
bolting	sheaf of straw normally weighing 14lbs but locally variable
booker	person responsible for keeping records of hops picked by each picker
bowler	chock to prevent wagon running backwards downhill (sometimes called a slipper)
BPP	British Parliamentary Papers
bract	individual sheath on the hop fruit containing the seed
burr	flower of the hop
bushel	dry (or liquid) measure of capacity equal to 8 gallons (36 litres)
catenary wire	support wire
charks	coke-like fuel produced from the sulphuric coal of south-west Worcestershire coalfields; the term has also been used for charcoal and the 'dead' coal on the edge of a fire
cranked hook	hook with an offset handle
crib	container into which hops were picked. Sacking was stitched onto a wooden frame
cutting	pruning hop plant back to the crown
didicoy	a travelling scrap dealer etc., not a true gypsy; the name has also been used locally for gypsies and tramps
dobbin	workhorse
EHF	Experimental Husbandry Farm
faggot	bundle of sticks bound together and used as fuel
fat hen	*Chenopodium album*
flags	pieces of hop bine remaining on the top wire after the bine has been pulled
FYM	farm yard manure
gapping up	replanting hops where previous ones had perished
green sack	sack into which hops were measured for transport to the kiln

green stage	a staging built against the outer wall of the kiln, with a slatted floor, to keep the sacks of green hops fresh until they can be loaded into the kiln
grubbing	removing, digging out
half crib	crib with division in the middle for two separate pickers
hill	flat-topped mound on which the hop was grown
HMB	Hops Marketing Board
hogshead	54 gallons
hooker	long-handled tool, similar to a pruner, used for attaching hooks to the top wire
hop acre	ground covered by 1000 hop plants, used as a measure for piece-work. In Herefordshire in the 1890s there were 1500 to 1600 hills to the statute acre. Many growers made their returns by hop acres, not by statute acres
hop garden	Kentish term for hopyard
hopping	hop picking
hopping rate	the proportion of hops used in brewing determined in lbs per barrel or grams per hectolitre
hopyard	hop field
house	section of hopyard
hurricane lamp	paraffin lamp with a glass covering to prevent flame from being blown out
kell	kiln
kerf	stocker, hoe shaped drawhoe
kill	kiln
kiln hair	large mat of woven horsehair on which hops were placed for drying
leafing	removing lower leaves on the bine, nowadays usually by chemical defoliant sprays
Lent grain	spring wheat
megger	electronic instrument for measuring moisture content of pocketed hops
monkey	long rod to guide the string from peg to top hook
mould	a common fungal disease
oasthouse	Kentish term for hop kiln, used generally in the south east region
piece	bread and jam
platens (plattens)	perforated metal strips forming the bottom of a drying bin or kiln floor, which can be tilted by an external lever so that the hops drop through to a lower tier
plenum chamber	part of hop kiln – the chamber below the drying floor
ploughing down	removing soil from hops back towards middle of row
ploughing up	returning soil to cover he base of the hop plant, to smother weeds and encourage strong cuttings
pocket	long sack, approx 6 feet of closely woven jute into which hops were pressed and then marketed

pole puller	originally man who pulled the pole out of the ground in pole-work; after wirework was introduced the name was retained for men overseeing picking
pole-work	system of supporting hops on thin poles
quassia	bark or root, used as an insecticide
reek	condition fault caused by too high a temperature, or too low an airspeed in the initial stages of drying when moisture will condense onto the hops giving them a dullish colour.
roller hair	method to simplify emptying single tier kilns (photo p.154)
rood	¼ acre
scuppet	wooden shovel for moving hops in the kiln
sett	cutting taken from a plant when cutting and throwing down, to be replanted perhaps in a nursery
shoddy	shredded rag, waste product of woollen and carpet industry, used as organic fertilizer
slag	sometimes known as basic or basic slag – waste material from blast furnaces applied as a phosphate fertilizer
slinger	unsupported pocket held only by ropes on a lorry load of hops
slipper	see bowler
soller	loft, upper room
spiky, spike heads	appearance of a stunted growing tip suffering from downy mildew
spray	side shoot on which the hops are produced (also called a lateral)
squat	to immobilize a wheel with a bowler or chock
stocking away	see throwing down
strig	stem of hop
tallet	hayloft
tatting cart	rag and bone man's handcart
throwing down	removing the soil from around the plant in spring, preparatory to cutting and tying
tines	slender prongs
tod, todd	unit of weight used for small load of wool etc weighing 28 lb, also used for the handful of dried hops sewn into the bottom corners of a hop pocket to facilitate handling.
top-hook	hook fixed to the top wire over which the hop string is run
treading hole	hole in hop-room or farmhouse floor from which a pocket was suspended for a man to tread hops into the pocket, before the advent of hand-operated mechanical presses
tumped	piled in heaps
wainhouse	shed for wagons and carts
wilt tolerant	hop variety showing degree of resistance to verticillium wilt
wires	alternative word for bines, especially in the early stages of growth
wirework	framework of permanent wires to support strings for hops to climb
zentner (ztn)	50 kg or 110.23 lb (originally 100 German pounds, an inexact measure redefined as exactly 50 kilograms)

INDEX

Parishes outside Herefordshire are identified by county